Loving Trees is Not Enough:

Loving Trees is Not Enough:

Communication Skills for Natural Resource Professionals

Brooks C Mendell, Ph.D.

Aventine Press

Published by Aventine Press
1023 4th Ave #204
San Diego CA, 92101
www.aventinepress.com

ISBN: 1-59330-428-5

Printed in the United States of America

Table of Contents

Preface

Early in my forestry career, I learned that working with trees is really about working with people. One morning, as a young forestry assistant at a logging operation in Raymond, Washington, I used a region-wide radio to inform a crew leader about a problem with the truckloads coming from his job. In other words, I used a bullhorn to tell the guy his fly was open. Soon, several truck drivers let me know this person was upset. That day, I apologized to him. He explained to me that it wasn't what I had to communicate, but how I did it that upset him. He suggested that, should there be a next time, I tuck a brief written note away with one of the truck drivers returning to the woods, or, better yet, come deliver the message myself.

Working as a forest industry researcher reinforced for me how clients, managers, and colleagues hear information and learn concepts differently. A paper industry executive in York, Pennsylvania once asked me to "please put that picture into words" while a timberland investment client from San Francisco requested that I "put those words and numbers into graphs and pictures." The obligation falls on the messenger to package information in a manner that communicates clearly to the intended audience.

Successful natural resource professionals communicate well. They inspire others, create cooperation between colleagues, advocate ideas and proposals, educate students and community members, negotiate contracts, and conduct and participate in interviews. Gary Brett, a forest business owner in north Florida, told a group of forest resource students in 2005, "I encourage you, do anything you can do to develop your communication skills, your people skills. It's about who can get things done, and that's about working with people." This underlies the central themes of this book: how we communicate and what we communicate drives our careers and personal relationships.

Research into the skills required by college graduates emphasizes the importance of professional interactive skills. The National Association of Colleges and Employers found that employers across industries rank interpersonal skills first, followed by the ability to work in teams and verbal communications skills as the most preferred traits for new employees (NACE 2001).

However, studies also indicate that college graduates lack necessary communication skills. Morgan (1997) found opportunities for more explicit communication skills training and practice for accounting students in the United Kingdom. Peterson (1997) surveyed personnel interviewers at businesses in the Midwest. Approximately 40% felt that current job applicants demonstrated inadequate communication skills, particularly in areas such as eye contact, listening skills, and the clarity and relevance of their responses to questions.

Why do prospective employees lack these skills? Researchers point to a number of possible reasons. Learning had become too passive, effectively leaving few opportunities for students to actively develop communication skills (Garside 2002), while formal classroom presentations alone provide insufficient training for workplace communicating (Crosling and Ward 2002). In practice, the informal nature of most workplace communications points to a need to practice in a range of settings.

These studies affirm that not only are communication skills in demand, they remain important and relevant throughout one's career. Regardless of your discipline or technical skills, the legacy you leave and the reputation that precedes you stem from your ability to communicate.

The title for this book was inspired by physicist Peter Feibelman's book *A Ph.D. Is Not Enough! A Guide to Survival in Science* (1993, Perseus Publishing). His book succinctly addresses topics specific to academic careers that include giving research talks and interviewing for research jobs. I acknowledge the assumption implied in his title and how it inspired the title for this book: being effective and successful in our fields requires skills beyond the technical. For foresters and other natural resource professionals, our love of and experience with trees and wildlife do not guarantee our ability to manage, persuade, or educate effectively. Rather, this depends on our ability to communicate what we know to others.

This book aims to introduce and reinforce fundamental communication skills, regardless your current skill level. The communication skills addressed in this book focus on six areas:

- Professional and educational presentations to groups,
- Formal job or informational interviews,
- Salary negotiations,
- Electronic communications using phones, cell phones, and email,
- Group meetings, and
- Feedback to employees and between colleagues.

The following provides a more detailed description of the topics by chapter:

Chapter One, *Public Speaking*, covers the responsibilities and skills required to present information to groups in public speaking settings. The chapter includes a preparation guide that can be used for any presentation, and it explicitly details an approach for fielding questions and providing answers during or after presentations.

Chapter Two, *Interview Skills,* deals with the skills for participating in interviews, and for writing resumes and cover letters. Often, we default to "job interviews." However, the interview process requires similar preparation and skills whether it is in pursuit of a job, gathering information, or speaking with clients regarding ongoing projects. This chapter also discusses, with examples, resumes and cover letters.

Chapter Three, *Negotiating*, focuses on salary negotiations. Negotiating a salary, whether for a first time job or for a pay increase, relies on practical preparation to determine your market value. Then, understand your priorities, remain positive, listen carefully, and get it in writing.

Chapter Four, *Phones, Cell Phones, Voicemail, and Email,* explores the realm of electronic communications. This includes proper etiquette for phone calls and cell phones, a professional approach for using voicemail, and guidance on scripting and using email. Experience tells us we pick up and start using these tools without realizing their unintended consequences or appropriate ways to use them.

Chapters Five and Six address topics of increasing importance as you move forward and advance in your career. Chapter Five, *Meetings*, discusses workplace meetings. Meetings generate resentful feelings when poorly managed or scheduled without concrete objectives. This chapter addresses the issues associated with properly planning, managing, and participating in meetings. The less time we spend in meetings, the more time we can spend in the field, working with clients, doing our jobs, and being with our families.

Chapter Six, *Giving Feedback*, addresses the giving of job-related feedback. This includes feedback to those that work for you and those that work with you. Both what we say and how we say it really matters at work and at home. Ultimately, we seek to avoid surprises by clearly and continuously communicating expectations, standards, concerns, and appreciation.

Why do natural resource professionals need their own book about communication skills?

- One, I wish I had had one earlier in my career, to summarize communication issues with an appreciation for natural resources. While most communication skills apply universally, we use these skills within the context of our professions. Therefore, learning about communicating within a natural resource context speeds our understanding and adoption of these skills.

- Second, programs in natural resources have fewer courses focused on developing communication skills than professional programs in business or law. Surveys of firms hiring into forest resource fields confirm the need for college graduates and professionals who can, among other things, integrate sound ethical principles, work in teams, listen to and address public and client questions, communicate orally and in writing, and manage people (Brown and Lassoie 1998; Sample et al. 1999; Thompson et al. 2003; Mendell 2005). Also, state resource agencies seek these skills in new employees who must increasingly interact with citizens and the media.

- Third, natural resource professionals communicate with a broad range of groups and individuals. We work with students, researchers, private consultants, industry members, non-profits, local and federal governments, community groups, and our neighbors. Often, folks just want to know what we are up to, and we owe it to them to be able to explain what we are doing, why we are doing it, and how it will help or affect them. In many ways, our communication skills are applied in a wider array of settings than those of a lawyer, doctor, or teacher.
- Finally, we may think that strong technical skills in our respective disciplines will carry us through our careers. Unfortunately, strong technical skills may not even get us a job. If they do, technical skills divorced from the ability to communicate that we have these skills, and what we're doing with them, may limit our options and ability to influence team or firm decisions.

Who should read this book? In a general sense, anyone looking for guidance to improve his or her communication skills. Specifically, this book targets natural resource students and active natural resource professionals and managers – those in forestry, wildlife, fisheries, hydrology, environmental education, outdoor recreation – who want to better understand and improve their workplace communication skills.

How should it be used? This book may be used two ways. It is ordered to provide a logical sequence for a semester long course or seminar in communication skills. Thus, it can provide the basis for a class. Alternatively, the chapters stand on their own; one can turn directly to the specific topics of interest, as outlined in the table of contents.

Acknowledgements

Several colleagues and family members reviewed earlier drafts of *Loving Trees is Not Enough* and provided helpful feedback and suggestions. In particular, I want to thank my aunt, grammarian and teacher, Susan Brooks and former Chair of the Communications Committee for the Society of American Foresters and retired communications professional Dick Reid. Both provided detailed edits and ideas to improve the readability of the content. Thank you to my in-laws, Michigan State University Professor Larry Schiamberg and Gale Schiamberg, who drew on their textbook writing experiences to improve the structure of the book. Thank you Brenda Golbus, Gale's twin, for her help with the literature citations. Thank you to organizational performance and executive development expert, Dr. Marc Gamson, for helping focus the final draft to the intended audience. Thank you to my parents, Barbara and Steven Mendell, for their suggestions, edits, and encouragement. Finally, I want to thank my wife, Liz, and our baby girl, Dani, for their continued, well-communicated support.

We do not live in a vacuum. Rather, we come to understand each other and ourselves by how we interact in groups, and with natural resources. And we offer a great gift when we can communicate our ideas and feelings clearly and effectively. This book aims to help us accomplish this.

Literature Cited

Brown, T.L., and J.P. Lassoie. 1998. Entry-level competency and skill requirements for foresters: what do employers want? *Journal of Forestry* 96(2):8-14.

Crosling, G. and I. Ward. 2002. Oral communication: the workplace needs and uses of business graduate employees. *English for Specific Purposes* 21:41-57.

Garside, C. 2002. Seeing the forest through the trees: a challenge facing communication across the curriculum programs. *Communication Education* 51(1):51-64.

Mendell, B.C. 2005. Integrating communications training into the forestry curriculum. Proceedings of the Society of American Foresters National Convention, Washington, D.C. 6 p (available on CD ROM).

Morgan, G.J. 1997. Communication skills required by accounting graduates: practitioner and academic perceptions. *Accounting Education* 6(2):93-107.

National Association of Colleges and Employers (NACE). 2001. The job market for the class of 2001. Planning job choices. 44th ed. Bethlehem, PA.

Peterson, M.S. 1997. Personnel interviewers' perceptions of the importance and adequacy of applicants' communication skills. *Communication Education* 46:287-291.

Sample, V., P. Ringgold, N. Block, and J. Giltmier. 1999. Forestry education: adapting to the changing demands on professionals. *Journal of Forestry* 97(9):4-10.

Thompson, J.R., J.P. Colletti, S.E. Jungst, and B.L. Liklider. 2003. Preparing tomorrow's foresters: embedding professional interactive skills in a technical discipline. *Journal of Forestry* 101(7):8-13.

Chapter 1:
Public Speaking

When I ask you to listen to me
and you start giving advice, you have not done what I asked.
from "Listening" by Ralph Roughton

Speaking begins with listening. Speaking publicly is a responsibility; it's a responsibility we accept when we have something to say. This involves a relationship between you, the speaker, and an audience that grants you its time and attention. Accepting this responsibility begins with listening to learn the interests, needs, and wants of our audiences.

When we speak, we often speak to an audience of individuals who did not ask to hear us. We enter an arranged relationship where our value may never be explicit, but where we can always show that we take the responsibility of speaking, of listening to our audience, seriously. Therefore, in preparing for talks, we seek to ensure a practical and meaningful connection where value has been added to the audience. At its most basic level, this preparation boils down to three themes: know your purpose, know your audience, and know your message. These themes provide a framework for each speaking engagement to answer the question, "Am I prepared for this talk?"

KNOW YOUR PURPOSE (the "why?") Addressing students, clients, or colleagues requires preparation. Your audience grants you license to borrow time, a license to speak with the option to speak again. The single most important thing to know is why you are there. What is your purpose in front of this group? Generally, this falls into one of three main categories: to educate, to entertain, or to persuade.

By definition, teachers educate, comedians entertain, and politicians persuade. In practice, most presentations are a combination of the three. The comedian Will Rogers said, "I don't make jokes. I just watch the government and report the facts." His primary purpose, to entertain, included educating and updating his public on current events. Regardless the combination, each presentation derives its focus from a central, core purpose.

Sometimes, when making introductions or toasts, your job is to be forgotten. Introductions introduce a speaker or guest to an audience; they are not mini-speeches. If you know the speaker, share a brief story. A proper toast honors a person or event, not the toast maker. (Remember that before sharing an untested joke or risqué story.) Awards banquets go awry, for example, when award presenters hijack unavailable time for unrelated commentary or drawn-out stories. Support the main event; do not disrupt or distract from it.

Effective impromptu comments benefit from the PREP approach suggested by Toast Masters International, a non-profit organization dedicated to developing public speaking skills (www.toastmasters. org). PREP stands for Point, Reason, Example, Point. Make a point, state the reason for the point, give an example that supports the point, and close by restating your key point. Once, a client, who was a baseball fan, questioned the value (and cost) of annual training. I shared this example with him:

Point: "Professionals at all levels practice basic skills."
Reason: "We practice these skills to keep them fresh, kind of like 'use it or lose it.'"
Example: "Look at pro baseball players. Every spring, pitchers practice covering first base on ground balls hit to the right side of the infield. And these are the best players in the world."
Point: "We are professionals and we train annually to keep these skills sharp."

Using a structured approach, like PREP, helps organize thoughts to meet the needs of the occasion, particularly in impromptu speaking situations. Think about how this approach could improve meetings. How often have we listened to people ramble on in meetings without making logical sense or contributing useful points? The

PREP framework and approach reduces anxiety and increases the effectiveness of your comments by removing the need to figure out how to start, organize, and end. Having a framework in mind to organize impromptu comments lets you focus on the purpose: contributing an effective argument.

When we clearly understand and explicitly specify why we are standing before an audience, we take the first step in preparing ourselves to organize our thoughts and contribute. To maintain the level of self-awareness required to add value to the audience, know your purpose.

KNOW YOUR AUDIENCE (the "who?") Why present if the audience fails to listen? It's your responsibility to identify a connection to their interests and to hold their attention. Fortunately, your audience, whether voluntary or involuntary, usually wants to hear what you have to say. And you can further involve an audience with eye contact, rhetorical questions, and personal anecdotes or experiences. However, to truly engage an audience, you must take an interest in them. First, learn about the audience in advance. Second, read and react to your audience while speaking.

To properly prepare your speech, make time to learn about your audience. Understand the age, experience, and priorities of the group. On the first day of a graduate course called Financial Statement Analysis, Professor Brett Trueman, having never met us, called each one of the 35 students by name. In a few cases, he referenced our undergraduate institutions or previous occupations. At the end of that first class, he said, "You see how hard I prepare for you. Please prepare for me, as well." Professor Trueman earned instant respect through his preparation.

While often impractical to learn the name, date of birth, and social security number of each person in the room, we can learn about the audience's situation in advance, and how what we have to say takes the experience of the audience into account. This reminds us of the old story of the flood consultant who told Saint Peter with confidence that he would share with the assembly in heaven how he handled the great Johnstown flood of 1988...until he learned that Noah would be in the audience. We can always learn enough to localize our message and establish that we did our homework and tailored our talk to the group.

Effective speaking includes making real-time adjustments to your audience. On one occasion, I was in Dallas to give a lighthearted presentation about trees to conclude a gathering of forest industry consultants. The day's events had run over, pushing the start of my talk later into the evening. My role was to lighten the mood, not fill a time slot. Putting myself in the audience's shoes, I knew they were tired. Before starting, I cut half of the material and focused on being high energy for a few key examples and stories.

Knowing your audience is the quickest way to earn credibility. Audiences appreciate well-prepared and authentic presentations that meet their specific needs. Know your audience.

KNOW YOUR MESSAGE (the "what?") Knowing your message means understanding how you add value to an audience. A former colleague of mine once told me, as we debated the results of the 2000 U.S. Presidential election, "Look, the basic bargain of our democracy is this: what matters is who inspires others." This gets at the value you bring to an audience. How does your message influence and improve the audience's situation?

Be able to state your take-home message in one clear sentence. An Atlanta-based radio personality who hosted a Sunday morning show on plants and trees ended each show with, "Remember, green side up, brown side down, and tell your family that you love them." Mom, a League of Women Voters volunteer in California, teams up with a partner to speak about ballot referendums. Their message: there are two sides to every issue, and here are current examples.

Know your message and how to communicate it clearly. One of the biggest mistakes presenters make is including too many details, which pulls the audience away from the main message. Listeners get lost in technical examples and complicated story lines. It is your responsibility to stay on topic and help your audience focus.

Part of knowing your message is being prepared, which gives you chances for true spontaneity. Years ago, Dad used to herd the family into the living room to practice presentations for work. He would show slides on the living room wall with graphs and pie charts, and go so far as to thank the person who would be introducing him. "Thank you, Carol for that introduction...." ("Who's Carol?" we would ask.) Due to his careful preparation, Dad could leave his prepared comments to comfortably answer questions, add timely insights, or respond to audience feedback.

Of course, knowing your message differs from successfully delivering this message. Dedicate time to develop an effective introduction and snappy conclusion. People pay attention to the first thing you say and, if they stay in the room, the last thing you say. Introducing new ideas or arguments at the end drowns out the work conducted in presenting the bulk of the talk. An introduction that fails to engage the audience and explain the topic misleads the audience. If nothing else, get the introduction and the conclusion right, and do cartwheels in the middle.

Effective presentations require practice and knowing how you add value. What skill, knowledge or feeling will you transfer to the audience through your presentation? Know your message.

In sum, preparing to speak makes you isolate what you think and why, and how you will explain it. When giving a talk, always consider – listen to – the audience, and what you want them to walk away with. Knowing your purpose, audience, and message demonstrates accepting the responsibility of speaking to and engaging a group. Choose to embrace these as opportunities and use the following guidelines to successfully communicate your message.

You and the Audience: Looking for Feedback

If we believe in the importance of actions, the audience members who read, play with cell phones, leave early, or sleep are telling us something. As audience members, we always have feedback for speakers, whether or not we give it to them. We form opinions on the effectiveness of the presentation, on the clarity of the message, and on the quality of the speaker's voice, clothes, and jokes. The speaker may make us laugh or cry. The speaker may anger us by going over the allotted time, or by demonstrating a clear lack of preparation. We always have feedback.

Examples are plentiful. A former finance professor of mine, an excellent teacher, had the distracting habit of clicking on and off the caps of his dry erase markers. A successful forest conservationist undermined a quality presentation by quoting, to a group of foresters, inaccurate facts about U.S. forests. An Economic Minister from Spain gave a commencement address by reading word-for-word a document that, clearly, someone else had written. A lackluster talk by a well-known actor and dancer became a dazzling presentation when he paused the talk to demonstrate an array of tap-dancing snippets. We notice what drives us to distraction.

As a speaker, this feedback can be extremely helpful and difficult to get. Therefore, we rely on our own observations and insights to extract from the audience this information. For example, laughter is great feedback, though smiles and nodding heads serve well, too. This information can guide the remainder of a current speech and improve the preparation for the next speech. I offer three practical examples of collecting real-time feedback from your audience while speaking:

Observe where the audience is sitting. Notice if the group occupies the front rows or fills in the back rows, leaving 80 empty seats between you at the front of the room and the audience. Notice if the members of the group spread out, creating a checkerboard of occupied seat, empty seat, occupied seat, empty seat, king me.

How can we use this information to improve a presentation? A scattered group changes the dynamics of the room. In cases where everyone chooses seats in the back, avoid the "Let's have everyone fill in the front rows" in favor of recruiting the group members to help you rearrange the room in a more favorable manner. Move extra chairs to the side or place the group in a circle. If handled politely, this provides an opportunity to interact with the group prior to speaking and builds group chemistry. Good blood flow helps brain flow, and encouraging active participation builds expectation and interest.

When teaching short courses, I encourage participants to introduce themselves and tell what they do and why they are taking the class. After the last person speaks, I make a few summary comments, noting common jobs or themes across the introductions. This presents an opportunity to demonstrate active listening and to learn a few personal things about the group that may provide connections later in the day. It also identifies those in the room who prefer quieter roles versus those who will actively engage in discussion. Forewarned is forearmed, and indications of where the group may need managing or support enables you to prepare for working with the group throughout.[1]

Also, check lines of sight to ensure that everyone can see you, and that you can see everyone. Like the bumper sticker on 18-wheelers that read "If you can't see my mirror, I can't see you," lack of eye-contact between you and the audience reduces valuable communication.

Observe where the audience is looking. At times you may look out into the audience and ask yourself, "Are they really looking at me, or looking past me?" After the introduction, actively observe where people are actually looking. At this point, you have had a chance to introduce the theme and the audience has had a chance to size you up. Audience members begin deciding whether or not your presentation is going to be worthwhile and interesting, or whether a permanent bathroom break is in order.

We observe audience glances to assess audience engagement. Are you and your slides holding their attention? In addition, the conscious observation of audience eyes ensures that you are making eye contact with the audience, a key indicator of successful presentations.

Observe what the audience is doing. And comment on it. This includes eating, doodling, passing notes, checking email on

Blackberries, and playing solitaire on Palm Pilots. Speakers and lecturers face an uphill battle against an increasing number of intrusive electronic gadgets that can distract audience members and their neighbors. Part of the reason folks bring these devices into the room is because they have come to develop low expectations of what lectures, presentations, and meetings will offer them. For a new audience, then, the battle is not really between you and the audience or you and their gizmos. Rather, it is your message versus their expectations.

As in observing eye contact, observing actions can guide you mid-talk, indicating the need to take action. Reengaging the audience requires intervention. Adjust the rhythm, theme, and energy level of your presentation. Insert breaks or ask questions. Use your voice as an instrument by talking softer or changing tone. Stand on top of a desk, jump up and down, or recite a poem. Hand out candy or stop talking. Observing audience actions provides a litmus test to trigger a needed response when Joey in the back breaks out a meatball sub and bag of chips.

Delivery and Style

There is a mindset associated with effective speaking. It comes through your delivery and style in front of the room. Your style includes your comfort with standing in front, your confidence in the material, and your attitude and sense of humor. Talk with the audience, not at them; have fun with the audience, don't make fun of them; get angry with the audience, not at them. Effective speaking reflects effective management of the feel and flow in the room.

Teachers can do this by working through examples with a class. As a young procurement forester attending a Master Timber Harvester training session in Macon, Georgia, I listened to John Murphy give a talk on managing water quality and runoff from logging operations. "Be the water," he said, telling us to stand on the logging job and look around. Imagine a hard rain and where the water will go. Will it run down a slope, unimpeded, into a stream or onto a street? Will the water disperse systematically among the brush and streamside management zones? If there is opportunity for water to flow, it will. If the consequences are going to be undesirable, we must manage them. John helped us imagine what we would do as the water, a relatively new-age experience for a group of loggers and foresters, and taught an approach for managing and trouble-shooting harvest operations.

The style you bring to the stage and the way it informs your delivery have practical implications on the quality of your speaking. Before taking the stage, empty your pockets of excessive change and large masses of keys. The sound of tinkling change and rattling keys detracts and distracts from the talk. Remove big high school or college rings if you will be speaking from a podium. At times, speakers knock their rings rhythmically on the wooden dais, unaware of how a microphone amplifies this habit. Meet the audience, if possible, in advance of speaking. Go to the bathroom, and check your teeth and your fly. Have a colored pen nearby for last minute edits (green or red work well). You never know when inspiration or realization will strike. Last minute edits in the same color ink as the original text of your speech may be overlooked and missed during the delivery.

When taking the stage, survey the scene. This is the audience's first look at you as the speaker, and your comfort and confidence should be clear. Buz Williams, my high school football coach, would tell the quarterbacks to walk confidently to the line of scrimmage behind the center and survey the defense, like a boxer entering the ring. You begin to speak when YOU are ready.

Successful speaking depends on energy and content. If using written text, set it down while speaking; if using note cards, number them lest they fall. Beware memorizing speeches (it's easy to get off track by forgetting one phrase or key point). Please, PLEASE, banish disclaimers, such as "I'm not feeling well today" or "My slides are out of order." The audience does not know until you tell them. SO DON'T! They don't care. Whenever I hear a speaker make a needless disclaimer, I want to say "Then go home and come back when you're ready!" or "Thanks for telling us that we were not important enough to prepare for." Soldier on and do your best. Be comfortable with your material and have strength and energy in your purpose. This carries the day, regardless the quality of the PowerPoint or handouts.

Oh, and one more thing. Don't say "one more thing." Last minute, off the cuff additions to your argument and presentation sabotage the overall argument. They are rough, marginally considered, and ill-advised. The moment you think "oh, and one more thing," just say "thank you" and sit down.

Handling Questions and Answers During and After Your Speech

In 1995, while working out of the Raymond, Washington logging operations for Weyerhaeuser, I heard how the Raymond Sawmill manager stood before a room of union employees and staff, and invited the group to ask any question whatsoever. Questions challenged company strategy, overtime pay, benefits, and more. While describing the experience akin to standing before a firing squad, he also specified the necessity and importance of conducting such question and answer sessions. "If you don't know what you're talking about, you should not be in front of the room." As a leader, he recognized that your ability to interact with an audience is always being evaluated.

Encouraging and answering questions from the audience completes a presentation. It ensures that legitimate, two-way communication takes place and injects energy and anticipation into the room. Why? Because most Q&A sessions are unscripted, and one never knows the question or the answer. It is the first true opportunity for the audience to judge whether or not you know what you are talking about.

Specific recommendations and procedures can improve your approach and handling of questions and answers following a talk.

1. *Repeat, or restate, each question.* The audience wants to know what you've been asked. In groups larger than two, there is no guarantee everyone heard the question. You confirm your understanding of the question, and create space to consider an answer. If unclear, ask for clarification. Do not say, "That's a

good question" – it implies that one might also say "that's a bad question."

2. *Reflect on the question.* Pause. Breathe. It shows respect for the questioner and gives time to confirm your understanding of the question and to organize your thoughts. If still unsure of the point of the question, restate the question or ask for clarification. Pausing also helps minimize the "ums" and "ahs" that distract and weaken any response you provide.

3. *Answer the question.* Have you ever felt that a speaker did not answer the questions? Do not be that person. Keep answers brief and to the point. Maintain eye contact with the questioner and with the audience in general. Looking at just the questioner neglects the rest of the group, and makes the questioner feel like you are drilling holes through her head. After answering the question, consider following up, "Have I answered your question?" Coming back to the questioner gives you the opportunity to see if she is happy with your answer, and may encourage a follow-up question. If the person is hostile or chatty, do not follow up. Rather, make eye contact with someone else to end a one-on-one debate and draw other people into the discussion.

In sum, the recipe for answering questions is *Repeat, Reflect* and *Answer.*

Additional general guidelines can help you prepare and use specific strategies for dealing with particular situations. For example, postpone questions aimed at resolving specific problems or that seem off topic until the end of the talk. This is particularly important if the answer would break the general flow of your presentation. "I can better answer that question one-on-one. Let's discuss that afterwards...."

If you can't answer a question, say so. Don't apologize. Never bluff. You may offer to research an answer and get back to the questioner later. If you offer to do this, make sure you follow through. Ultimately your reputation and integrity rest on doing what you say you will do.

Alternately, suggest resources to help questioners find answers themselves or ask for suggestions from the audience. Often, OFTEN, someone in the room knows the answer or is familiar with a resource that can help. Be comfortable with asking for ideas from the group, and thank the person for his willingness to help. Remember, for a student or shy member of the audience, speaking out may represent a major effort and contribution.

When teaching, write down the question and, if it's relevant, answer it at the beginning of the following class. Often, these questions add to your own understanding. In short courses, track questions on a flip chart near the front of the room, and check them off if answered during the day. If not, look up answers following the short course and send the responses in a well-written, proof-read email or mailing to all of the attendees.

If you field a hostile question, be respectful and control emotional responses. Audiences, in general, do not like open attacks on polite, respectful speakers, and you can win the sympathy of the audience by remaining under control. Focus on the issues raised in the question, and respond with facts. Never engage in one-on-one debate or personal confrontation in front of the group. Depending on the situation, you might offer to discuss the issues with the questioner after the presentation, or ask the group for their responses to the question.

Allow questioners to finish asking their questions. Again, this shows respect for the audience member. Listen actively. Establish eye contact and focus on the questioner while he asks his question. Sometimes, there is no question. If necessary, tactfully break off a vague, rambling question (you have only limited time). For example, try "So, are you asking ....?" This focuses the question and gives a place to begin an answer. If the person appears to be talking to talk, ask sincerely, "what is your question?" or say, "I'm not sure I understand your question."

Inform the audience up front how you to intend to handle questions. Will there be a designated time for questions towards the end, or will you encourage and invite questions throughout the presentation? Your decision on how to handle this depends on your overall comfort with the material and the audience and the purpose of your talk. If the presentation is tightly scheduled and getting through the material is necessary, postponing questions until the end may be best. When giving a lecture, answering questions along the way to redefine terms or provide additional examples can help students digest difficult concepts. Taking questions during the talk also provides a barometer of success with the group. Is the message and material taking hold, or do we need to further explore this next time? Also, your ability to handle questions throughout emphasizes your journey WITH the audience, as opposed to talking AT them.

Anticipate questions throughout your preparation. Write down the questions, and potential responses, you will most likely be asked. Spend time especially on those questions you would least like to be asked, and those you would ask yourself if you were in the audience. Once you think, "I hope they don't ask me that," assume you will be asked that and consider your response. Practice an actual answer and determine what your point of view is on that issue.

When closing, notify the audience that the next question will be the last one. After answering it, close by making a transition back to the overall objectives of your talk and then summarize the key messages and next steps. And thank the audience. Etiquette matters.

Rules to Speak By

This section summarizes the key points of the chapter and highlights practical strategies associated with preparing, practicing, and presenting your speech. When in a hurry, refer to this section to refresh your memory. It is meant to provide the rapid fire summary needed when buckling down to actually prepare and give a talk.

PREPARING THE SPEECH
Start early. Generate ideas and stories and ways of presenting the material. Creativity has a way of percolating to the surface, to your conscious thought, given enough time. Understand the purpose, audi-

ence, and message for the talk. [See Appendix 1: Speech Preparation Guide]

Develop clear transitions. It's your job to help the audience follow the presentation. Pose questions or summarize themes. Be explicit.

Summarize. Do your audience a favor by reviewing and summarizing key points. When concluding, let your audience know "in summary." Announcing the conclusion helps the audience focus in and retain your final message.

Review the agenda. Know your place and your role. As a speaker, follow the host's agenda. If you are presenting one of many awards at an awards banquet, it's not your job to tell stories and speak for twenty minutes.

Prepare your introduction. When someone else will be introducing you, prepare a brief bio and suitable introduction for him or her to use. Include the phonetic spelling and pronunciation of your name. Review this with your presenter beforehand. Face it, we all hate hearing our names mispronounced.

PRACTICING THE SPEECH
Practice out loud, standing, with a stopwatch.

Practice out loud, in front of a mirror, with a stopwatch. Imagine making eye contact with your audience. Figure one-half double-spaced page per minute. Speak slowly. Much faster and the audience won't absorb what you're saying, especially for complicated arguments or technical talks.

Practice to yourself, with a stopwatch. Get the hint? Keep time. Don't run over! Ever! Shorten talks by reducing ideas, arguments or stories, not words. A stopwatch instills discipline and self-awareness.

Do a "speed through" to check your logic and thought process. Race through the key points of the speech, by memory, as fast as you can. Think about the logic and flow more and the actual words less. If you have difficulty remembering the key points in order, your brain may be telling you the order of the speech is illogical.

Practice with friends or colleagues, if possible, to gather helpful feedback for improving your presentation. Ideas that flow smoothly while flipping through notes can stumble sloppily and jaggedly when presented orally. A live rehearsal tests whether or not you understand what you want to say, and whether or not you say it in a manner clear to others. Also, this provides the means for identifying and eradicating distracting habits, such as mumbling or clicking pens. [See Appendix 2: Rehearsal Guide for making these practice sessions productive.]

Stay current. As you practice, check the accuracy of figures, comparisons, and analogies. If you are discussing a public company, know its current stock price and performance relative to the overall market. If you mention a foreign country, know its capital and current political situation, and the size of its economy relative to the U.S. If you cite a study, know the source and opposing view. Having today's news at your fingertips to provide relevancy and perspective shows you know what's going on in the world. Small efforts to stay current pay big dividends in credibility, especially during the question and answer session.

Visit the venue. If possible, visit and walk the room or stage in advance. Get a feel for its size, layout, and acoustics. Will the audience be seated above or below you? Will you be seated or standing? Walk from where you will be seated to where you will be speaking. Check on equipment and software and order of slides. Check the remote control. If help is needed, get it early.

TAKING THE STAGE

Empty your pockets. Remove keys and coins. Speakers will, through habit or nervousness, thrust hands in pockets and jiggle keys. Sometimes, speakers will slap their sides or pockets, striking coins. The noise of the coins or keys is a distraction and can be prevented by removing them from your pockets.

Remove big rings. Sometimes, speakers tap the podium when they speak. An anvil-sized school ring, tapped on the podium near the microphone, makes a loud thud. Don't do this. It's annoying and distracting. If in doubt, go without. Remove big rings.

Remove nametags. Look, you're in front! The audience should know your name if there's a program or if you have been introduced. If they don't, tell them, because they surely won't be able to read your nametag. If the tag is in a plastic sheath, common at conventions or seminars, it can reflect light and cause a glare. If it's a sticky type, it looks cheap. Remove nametags when speaking.

Go to the bathroom (even if you don't need to). Check zippers, buttons, and teeth. Blow your nose.

Survey the scene. Survey the scene as you take the stage. Take your time. You are in charge. Scan the faces and wait for chatter to die down. Take a breath and begin with energy. Start when YOU are ready.

Meet the audience. If possible, chat with and welcome members of the audience. Speaking with friends is easier than speaking to strangers.

Keep a colored pen nearby for real-time, last minute edits. Pre-speech additions or edits need the green or red ink to stand out from your prepared text while you speak. Keep the pen handy to record audience feedback or make notes during the Q&A.

SPEAKING

Speak with energy. Two things hold audience attention. Content and energy. A successful presentation needs at least one of these. Both make a winner. Final thought before speaking...ENERGY!

Be positive. Do not criticize or complain about the facilities, trip, or food. They don't care. Do not alienate the audience – they didn't choose the lunch menu, either.

Banish disclaimers. The audience does not want to know your weaknesses, problems, or excuses. They don't want to know why you are late, or that you "didn't have time to prepare," or that you're "not sure what to say" or that you forgot your slides. They don't know any of those things until you tell them. Don't tell the audience what you won't do; tell them what you will do. Do not apologize for anything.

Don't say "and one more thing." As soon as the urge to add something to a statement or answer arises, stomp it. Follow-ups weaken what was already said and will probably be said with less clarity than the key point. If a person from the audience wants to know more, he or she will ask. Avoid those unpracticed, impromptu additions, especially at the conclusion.

Avoid holding paper or cards. A modestly shaking hand becomes a noticeably trembling piece of paper, revealing a scared speaker. The audience does not want you to be nervous. If you need notes, organize them well and put them on a table or the podium. A single index card can efficiently carry a brief outline, but avoid holding more than one. Drop the cards and you're screwed. If you MUST hold cards, number them. Cards work well for slide shows – while the audience is focused on the screen, you are able to organize your thoughts with cards corresponding to the slides.

Beware laser pointers. They also reveal nervousness. Don't wave them around or point one at the audience. Turn on and off to highlight points. They are not light sabers and you are not Luke Skywalker.

Speak to the audience, not to the screen, when using PowerPoint or overhead slides.

ANSWERING QUESTIONS
Repeat each question. The audience wants to know what you've been asked.

Reflect on the question. This shows respect for the questioner, and gives you time to be sure you are answering the right question. If you are unsure, restate the question or ask for a clarification.

Allow the questioner to finish asking the question. At times, it becomes necessary to break off a vague, rambling question; you have only limited time to make your presentation. However, break in tactfully. Say something like "So, are you asking ....?" This brings focus to the question and gives you a place to begin an answer. Remember, your ability to interact with an audience is also being evaluated.

Postpone questions aimed at resolving specific problems until the end of the talk. This is particularly important if the answer will distract either you or the audience from the flow of your presentation. "I can better answer that question one-on-one. Let's discuss that afterwards...."

If you can't answer a question, say so. Don't apologize. You may offer to research an answer, get back to the questioner later, suggest resources to help the questioner find the answer himself, or ask for suggestions from the audience.

CONCLUDING

Conclude gracefully. When possible, and when appropriate, offer a final (and prepared) comment after the last question is answered. Briefly thank the audience and offer a closing thought related to your key message. This lets you end the presentation on your terms, regardless of the questions asked and your success in answering them.

Self assess in writing. Learn from each presentation. Once you sit down or have a moment alone, write down the two or three things that went especially well, and the two or three things that you would do differently. Wait too long and those fresh reactions fade from memory, lost until you repeat the same mistake again. Put a self-assessment in writing. It's how we learn.

FINAL THOUGHTS

You know your purpose, you understand your audience, and you believe in the value and relevance of your message to this audience. In preparing to speak, you recognized the responsibility and opportunity before you, and you embraced it. Consciously take the stage with confidence and energy. Your final thought before speaking....
ENERGY!

Appendix 1: Speech Preparation Guide

While preparing and before presenting your speech, be able to answer the following questions. When in doubt, follow up with the hosts or organizers. Having the answers to these questions builds confidence and puts you in control of your situation. When you understand what you are talking about and why, who you are talking to, and the logistic situation, the audience will sense your preparation and give you the benefit of the doubt.

1) What is the purpose of your talk? Why are you speaking?
   • Are you educating, entertaining, or persuading?

2) Who is your audience? How many people?
   • Men or women, young or old, friendly or hostile?
   • How much will they already know about your topic?
   • Why is the audience there? Work? Voluntarily?

3) What is your message? How do you add value?
   • Why is this message important to the audience?
   • Why are you qualified to present this message?

4) What is the schedule of events? When do you speak?
   • How long is your talk? Is Q&A time included?
   • Will there be other speakers?
   • If so, who are they and what will they be speaking about?

5) Where will the speech take place?
   • What is the layout of the room?
   • What type of equipment will be required?
   • Will you be sharing the stage with others?

Appendix 2: Rehearsal Guide

This rehearsal guide will help your friends and colleagues help you. It tells them what to look for while watching you practice, focusing on the areas that you can easily adjust. Effective rehearsals ask audience members for specific feedback against predefined criteria.

1) Introduction
- What you present
  i) Is your opening interesting?
  ii) Is your purpose defined?

- How you present it
  i) Do you appear confident?
  ii) Did you establish eye contact?

2) Body
- What you present
  i) Is the structure logical?
  ii) Is the content relevant and compelling?
  iii) Are transitions smooth?

- How you present it
  i) Is your voice clear and tone appropriate?
  ii) Any distracting mannerisms or body language?
  iii) Are visual aids, if any, explained well?

3) Conclusion
- What you present
  i) Is the close strong and concise?
  ii) Are the next steps clear?

- How you present it
  i) Are questions listened to? Answered?
  ii) Are you credible and convincing?

Chapter 2:
Interview Skills

Interviews are structured conversations for sharing information. Information gathered in interviews is used to make hiring decisions, conduct research, or write news articles. Successful interviews, whether you are the interviewer or interviewee, result from proper preparation, deliberate practice, and active listening. Failing to prepare is preparing to fail. This chapter details strategies, tools, and techniques to successfully prepare and participate in a range of interview situations.

Job Interviews: Getting the Job You Want

> *"A candidate who perceives employment as a training ground will not influence an employer to make an offer....Employers hire because they have a void... Applicants must demonstrate a genuine interest in filling the job that needs filling or they will be pounding the pavement for a long time!...college graduates who conduct a search in a targeted, businesslike way, and who have realistic expectations about the employer-employee relationship, will find no shortage of the jobs and salaries they are looking for."*
>
> Joyce M. Short, Executive Director
> National Career Network Division,
> American Career Council[2]

A job interview is a two-way street that seeks to answer two questions: Do you want this job? Do they want you for this job (or for a different job)? Information flows to both sides, and both sides hope to end the interview with the information they need to answer these questions. The first question determines your enthusiasm for this job, which is a function of how interested you are and how much you need the job. The second question captures the firm's enthusiasm for you and their assessment of whether or not you have the skills or potential to satisfy the needs of the role.

Interviews may be the most important event in your job search, and successful interviews result from proper preparation. This preparation includes:

- Researching the job and company you plan to interview with,
- Practicing the questions you will likely be asked,
- Understanding the needs and perspective of the interviewer,
- Following through on expected interview etiquette and practices, and
- Preparing and delivering the appropriate documents, such as resumes and thank you notes.

Why is this work necessary? An interview is an opportunity to develop a professional relationship with a prospective employer. This preparation helps build the confidence and gather the tools necessary to make the most it. As with any skill, interviewing requires learning what you need to do and practicing.

Ultimately, for the interviewee, the purpose of a job interview is to receive a job offer. Not receiving the offer does not mean the interview was a failure. Rather, the firm will know more about your skills and abilities for future roles, and you will have a better understanding of the organization and this type of job. Most importantly, you have a new contact. Conversations are interviews, and job interviews are really just structured conversations.

Succeeding in a job interview requires preparation to know why you are there and what will be expected of you. Understanding that you are there to obtain a job offer provides the needed focus. Preparation for the interview means understanding the proper professional etiquette for interviewing with this firm and identifying and practicing answering, and asking, questions. Your opportunity to ask questions provides the interviewer with insight into how you think, how you communicate, and how much you already know about his organization. In sum, it provides an opportunity to highlight your skills and showcase your research.

Before the Interview

Prior to an interview, include the following in your preparation:

Research the job for which you are interviewing, the company, and its operation. Know the exact names of contacts, the organization, and related departments. Know the job title and description for which you're applying. Knowing them shows that you are prepared and confident. Research also helps you develop good answers to the interviewer's questions.

Information you should know about the company prior to your interview:
- Current events and news about the company,
- Stock price and performance, if it is a publicly-traded firm,
- Products and services, especially new ones being developed,
- Company size and organizational structure, focusing on departments that interest you,
- How long they have been in business,
- Types of clients, and
- Geographic location of home office, branches, stores.

Resources for this information include:
- Company website,
- Company's annual report,
- Informational interviews, inside sources, and alumni,
- Newspaper and magazine articles, and
- Industry trade and professional associations.

To quickly become conversant on a company, whether for an interview or for research, follow this three-step procedure:

One, work the internet, beginning with the company website, if they have one, and then "Googling" the company name. Either way, this tells us something about the firm. Today, if a firm does not have a website, it is either too small, technologically out-of-touch, or extremely private. Small logging or manufacturing businesses may not have a compelling need to build and maintain a website, and learning about small private businesses depends on tapping into industry trade associations and people you know. For public companies, the websites provide consolidated summaries of products, services, locations, current events, and financial performance.

Two, read the annual report. While annual reports vary in quality, they provide excellent overviews of what a company does and how (and if) it makes money. Do not skip the introductory letter by the CEO, thinking it might be fluff. Read it first; this letter provides the CEO with the once-per-year opportunity to brag on accomplishments, address product or service failures, highlight major events, and introduce new personnel and offerings. The CEO always reviews the firm's strategy and may provide a useful summary of industry trends, as well. It goes without saying that the letter should be read with a grain of salt, but it is an excellent source for quickly learning what is important to the company and major positive and negative developments that occurred in the previous year.

Three, talk to people. For large firms in the forest industry, we often know someone who works for the firm, worked for the firm, interviewed with the firm, knows people at the firm, contracts with the firm, works for a competitor of the firm, or is a customer of the firm. When we put "contacts" into this context, we realize that we know more people and that we have more access to perspectives and first-hand information than we realize.

When arranging to visit and interview with a company, you may view yourself as the center of the universe. You focus on yourself, and companies and human resource managers are simply items on a checklist. However, consider the point of view of the firms and managers. To them, you are one of dozens or hundreds of potential job candidates. They must wade through reams of resumes and cover letters, gauge the value and relevance of recommendations and references, and winnow down lists of applicants to interview those with the highest potential. Should you make that final list, you MUST be familiar with the company prior to the interview. Go the website. Read the history, mission, and "about us" sections. Read the bios of the managers and be familiar with the services and product lines. Do this to be properly prepared and demonstrate true interest in the firm; it will separate you from other interviewees. Why? Because so few really learn about an organization prior to the interview.

Richard Bolles, author of "What Color is Your Parachute?" tells these two stories about the importance of studying a firm prior to interviewing:

> One time, the first question an IBM college recruiter asked a graduating senior was, "What do the initials IBM stand for?" The senior didn't know, and the interview was over.

> Another time, an employer said to me, "I'm so tired of job-hunters who come in and say, 'Uh, what do you do here?' that the next time someone walks in who already knows something about us, I'm going to hire him or her on the spot." And he did, within the week.

Prepare answers to typical interview questions. [See Appendix 2: Common Interview Questions] Study and practice your answers. The two most important questions are "Why this job?" and "Why this company?" If you cannot articulate why you want this job and why you want to work for this company, it indicates that you are not prepared and have not considered why you are interviewing for the job. Firms want to hire folks who are excited about this particular type of work. For these and other basic questions, prepare examples and practice answers aloud. Do not get caught by surprise here.

Prepare questions to ask the interviewer about the company. [See Appendix 1] Failure to prepare questions indicates a lack of knowledge and limited interest on the part of the interviewee. If you have read the annual report and visited the website, there will be things you may not understand or want to learn more about, such as company changes and new products. You will want to know what the job entails on a day-to-day basis, who you will be reporting to and working with, and what it takes to be successful in this job.

Memorize the name of the person who will interview you. A no-brainer. If you are unable to find this out in advance, write it down as soon as you meet the interviewer.

Confirm the time, date, and location of the interview. Schedules change and sometimes you are the last to know.

Decide what you will wear. (See "Dressing for the Interview" below.) Be sure your outfit is ready to go.

Find out exactly where to go, where to park, and how long it takes to get there. If traveling in an unfamiliar city, do a dry run prior to your interview. This alleviates undue stress the day of the interview. Know where you will park, how far the walk is from the building, and if there is a security guard (allocate time for this: they may need to call in to confirm that you are expected or to prepare a badge, or you may have to wait in line with others visiting the building.) Several times, I have been slowed at office building security desks to sign in and check out a visitor's badge. Managing this process is your responsibility.

Get a good night's sleep. Research confirms that well rested folks are more responsive and creative, and better able to deal with issues on the fly.

Arrive fifteen minutes early. This shows that you are prompt and gives you a chance to gain your composure. Be friendly to the receptionist or secretary. (Often, they are asked their opinion.) Bad things can happen if you are rushed, while good things are possible if you are early. For example, you may have more time to meet with the interviewer, meet other employees, hear or read important information which you can incorporate into your interview or receive an office tour. Locate the bathroom and check yourself in the mirror. Plus, the bathroom can tell you a few things about a company. Is it clean? Is there toilet paper? Does the hot water work?

Dressing for the Interview

Personal appearance and appropriate clothing are important in all interviews, especially with major corporations and firms that focus on client-based work. Dress conservatively by wearing a dark suit, minimal jewelry, conservative shoes, and coordinated accessories. Hairstyles should be professional, and cosmetics should be natural. Don't make a fashion statement unless you are fashion designer or pop star. Proper attire shows you take the opportunity seriously.

DOS and DON'TS

Do	Don't
• Dress conservatively	• Dress casually
• Practice good grooming (neat hair, clean hands, trimmed nails)	• Wear lots of jewelry (men: avoid earrings)
• Carry a portfolio or briefcase with extra resume copies	• Wear excessive cologne or heavy make-up
• Bring a notepad and pen that works	• Wear athletic shoes, mini-skirts, or Mickey Mouse ties
• Wear basic hosiery (no textured hose)	• Eat spicy smelling foods, garlic, or onions
• Wear comfortable, shined shoes	• Chew gum or smoke or dip
	• Carry a purse AND a briefcase

Frequently-Asked-Questions Regarding Professional Appearance

The following questions are frequently asked in class, during seminars, and in one-on-one conversations with respect to appearance:

What if I wear an earring, nose ring, or eyebrow ring?
What if I am a male with long hair?
What if my fingernails are painted a loud color?
Professional appearance standards vary by job, geography, and firm. If your appearance is not consistent with the local standard of the firm with which you're interviewing, you are unlikely to advance to the next stage. It is fair, in fact, for the interviewer to ask about your appearance, noting, for example, "You should know that a nose ring/ponytail/clearly visible ornamental object might not be acceptable in the office or with some of our clients. Are you opposed to removing it?" However, all things equal, you are better off knowing in advance what the standards are and, if you choose, be consistent with them when you attend the interview.

Do I have to wear a suit?
No. However, be appropriately dressed, neat, and well groomed. Suits are safe. For a job or informational interview, you cannot err by being overdressed. In forestry and natural resources, business casual attire, such as khakis or slacks and a button-down shirt or blouse, may still make you the best-dressed person in the office. Here are two versions of a common rule-of-thumb on this topic: Dress for the job you ultimately want in the future. (In other words, dress like the company president or department head.) Or, dress at least one level above the office norm. If everyone wears jeans to work, you wear slacks or khakis. If everyone wears business casual to work, you wear a suit, skirt or pantsuit. Either way, you separate yourself and demonstrate that you take the opportunity to visit and interview with the company seriously.

What if I have facial hair?

Acceptance of or indifference to facial hair differs across jobs and geography. In natural resource work, mustaches and beards are not uncommon and generally accepted, especially if trimmed and neat. For client-based jobs, tend towards the conservative. If your facial hair has religious or cultural meaning, or is required due to a medical condition, it should not be a concern. Determine the common practice and, if you have facial hair and want to keep it, be neat.

In the end, dressing for the interview means wearing clothes that do not detract from your professional appearance or distract the interviewers. Put yourself on the other side of the desk and think about questions the interviewers may ask themselves about you.

During the Interview: Interview Etiquette

Interview preparation and etiquette dictate much regarding your success or failure in an interview. Regardless of your skill level and past performance, bad breath or cheap perfume may effectively end the interview before it starts. For managers that have never met you or don't know you well, the interview represents their only first-hand exposure to how you conduct yourself, and this will determine how they believe you will perform on the job.

The beautiful thing about preparation, dress code, and etiquette: they are under your control. If there is a problem with your tie or your pen, you can replace them. If you have a hard time answering questions about your last job, you can prepare and practice, get guidance and advice from others. At this level, you are in control.

Start off strong. Offer your hand. Give a firm handshake (without cracking bones), a pleasant smile, and a positive confident attitude. Introduce yourself.

Be comfortable. Take a seat facing the interviewer, however, slightly off center. Be sure you are not facing into direct sunlight. Take the few moments you need to get comfortable and to properly situate your chair relative to the person across the desk. If you are sitting side-by-side, set your briefcase to the side.

Listen attentively. Look at the interviewer, but avoid a stare down. Sit up straight and relax. It's okay to take a few notes if the questions are lengthy, or if you need to remind yourself of something you want to stress. Maintain effective eye contact with the interviewer especially when making key points. Don't talk while the interviewer is talking.

Listening may be the most important skill a candidate brings to the interview. Often, successful interviews are those where you talk the least and listen the most. By talking through the interview, the interviewer indicates comfort and ease at being with you. For businesses that rely heavily on teamwork or for roles that deal directly with clients, your listening skills, the ability to actively pay attention and demonstrate that you understand what is being said (particularly if you understand that you do not understand exactly what the person means, and are able to ask clarifying questions) will represent a critical distinguishing characteristic between you and other candidates.

Avoid nervous mannerisms. Control nervous habits such as clicking your pen, twisting your hair, or biting your nails. Appear calm and collected.

Speak clearly. Use good grammar and a friendly tone. Never answer just "yes" or "no" to a question. A skilled interviewer wants you to do the talking. Clarify your answers, but do not ramble on. Be concise and give concrete examples.

Richard Bolles of "What Color is Your Parachute?" recommends the "twenty second to two-minute rule" when answering questions. This is similar to the elevator test, which says an entrepreneur or consultant should be able to succinctly and completely answer a question asked by an executive during an elevator ride. In an interview, a similar rule applies. The interviewer, who may have asked the same question of hundreds of applicants over the years, will be grateful for your clear answer supported with a relevant example from your direct experience.

Be positive and enthusiastic. No matter how sterling your credentials, you won't be hired if the interviewer does not feel positively towards having you join the organization. Prior to the interview, remind yourself why you are excited about this opportunity. Never whine, gripe, or complain about past employers, jobs, classes, etc.

Ask pertinent and thoughtful questions. Ask a few prepared questions. Avoid asking about salary and benefits; compensation related queries can be covered once you get an offer. While there are a range of things you may want to know, there are several items you NEED to know to develop an informed opinion about a job. These questions include:

- What does the job actually involve? You want a feel for what you will do day-to-day.
- What are the skills a top employee in this job needs? This will clarify what the firm values in terms of abilities and experiences, and provides an opportunity for you to match your current skills to where you would like to be in the future.
- Are these the kinds of people I would like to work with? Working with people you don't like or get along with makes life miserable, no matter how much money you are making.
- Can I persuade them to hire me at the salary I need or want? A question from Richard Bolles, it represents the bottom line of the interview process.

Watch for cues the interview is over. Don't linger if you sense the interviewer is done. When it is over, stand up, thank the interviewer for his time, and shake hands firmly.

Find out the next step. Do not leave an interview without learning the next steps in the process. If the interviewer does not volunteer this information (they may have forgotten, or they may not know), politely ask, "What's the next step?" or "What happens next?" Usually, the interviewer will tell you when his group plans to make a decision and contact you. The specific process varies widely by firm, from extremely structured and coordinated to informal and ad hoc. Make sure to ask when you can expect to hear from them.

After the Interview

Say "thank you." Write an actual thank you note to each person you interview with reiterating your interest in the job. Spell the interviewer's name correctly. The thank you note confirms your ability to communicate well, to operate in a professional environment, as well as showing your interest in the job. It also provides an opportunity to emphasize your strong points as they relate to the needs of the firm. Travel with stamps, note cards, and matching envelopes to write these notes that same evening back in the hotel room, or on the plane the next day.

Follow up. If you haven't heard from the interviewer within the time frame indicated at the close of the interview, call to politely remind him that you're still interested in the job. Ask when they plan to make a hiring decision.

Another way to follow up is to forward something, such as a news story or article, that relates directly to the conversation you had during the interview. In this way, you "add value" by putting something useful in the hands of the interviewer. If you aren't hired and the company still interests you, this approach provides another means for keeping in touch with the interviewer.

Stay positive. Prepare for your next interview. Contact the interviewer who rejected you and see if you can get any pointers on what to improve before your next interview.

Interviewer's Hidden Agenda

In Spring 2005, I met Bill, the former CEO of a Fortune 500 manufacturing firm. I asked him "What do you look for in a job candidate?" He said, "I look for two things: brains and urgency." As we talked about his ideal candidate, it became clear that this sense of urgency distinguished candidates because so few, in Bill's experience, truly responded or took action when it was required. He had a rule: all complaints, from customers or suppliers, receive a response that same day. Period.

Understanding what the employer looks for in a job candidate prepares you for the interview process, and enables you to decide whether or not you want to fill that role and accept its responsibilities. Put yourself in the shoes of the interviewer. A new hire represents a tremendous investment to a firm, one that requires time and resources to recruit, train, support, and make productive. You want to be seen as someone who brings solutions to problems and challenges the firm is facing. Understand the interviewer's perspective.

Employers may be uncertain and bewildered by the interview and hiring process, as well. This may be especially true of smaller natural resource firms and agencies that hire infrequently. In these cases, you will probably interview directly with the owner or a senior manager. In 2004, during a short course on communications skills, one owner of a small forestry consulting firm remarked, "Interviews are hard for me, too. It's hard to know the market and the salary expectations of recent graduates...."

There are questions that interviewers, by law, are not permitted to ask during an interview. These include questions about marital status, medical history, ethnicity, and age. [See Appendix 3 for examples.] When asked, how should you respond to inappropriate interview questions? First, recognize that, due to lack of training or experience, managers may not realize the impropriety of certain questions. Next, remain professional and consider asking, "How does this relate to the role I am interviewing for? Is it an area of concern?" It is possible the manager is trying to address a legitimate issue, but failed to do so properly. Alternately, if the manager persists in this line of questioning, it can raise a red flag and give you additional insight into whether or not you want to work for this firm. Regardless, be tactful in responding.

Interviewers have typical, common concerns that can be addressed directly when you answer questions. By being sensitive to these concerns, you can answer questions in the most positive and productive way for the interview. Generally speaking, these concerns can be grouped into three categories: technical skills, people skills, and the "bottom line."

Technical skills answer the question, "Does the applicant have the ability to do the job?" Underlying this question are targeted questions and concerns such as:

- What strengths does he or she have that we need? In other words, what value or help can you provide the day you walk in the door?
- In what areas is he or she weak? How will this affect performance? The interviewer and firm understand that training and time are required for a new team member to get up to speed. How much?
- What are his or her ambitions? Are they realistic? The interviewer wants a feel for how aware you are with respect to your skills relative to your goals. Do you understand your own strengths and weaknesses, and are you willing to do what is required to get the job done and to pursue your career goals?

In pursuing answers to these questions, interviewers are asking more situational and case questions to see if candidates do indeed actually have the skills required for the job.

People skills revolve around trust and confidence. Given the option, people work with people they like. Firms and teams depend on people they trust and can communicate with. Questions that help develop a picture of an interviewee's people skills include:

- How does he relate to people? The interviewer assesses the candidate's effectiveness in working with teams and colleagues.
- Can he manage people? The firm wants a sense of the candidate's growth potential and his ability to take responsibility for projects and teams. Carrying this line of queries forward, the interviewer wants to know, "What kind of person is this? A leader?"
- Would I put this person in front of clients and citizens? In natural resources, we spend time working with clients and public constituencies to define projects, to manage ongoing research, and to address concerns and questions. Your professionalism and ability to answer questions intelligently, without reaching beyond what you know, provide insight into your ability to represent the organization in public.
- How is the chemistry between us? Do I want to be around him? Hiring managers do not hire candidates who fail to listen, talk incessantly, or annoy them during the interview. Eight hours a day is a lot of time to spend with people you don't like.

The bottom line for the interviewer is "Should this person get an offer?" If the candidate lacks the technical and/or people skills needed for the job, the interviewer can quickly move to consider the next candidate. For applicants who (1) can help the organization by filling the role and (2) are the kind of person who the interviewer wants to work with, the question becomes, "How will other interviewers react?"

When someone asks for a recommendation, they are asking you to put your reputation on the line. Job applicants receive job offers because they are, in effect, recommended by the interviewers. If your colleagues recommend a candidate who eventually gets hired, and the person turns out to be a poor hire, this reflects on the interviewers. People make mistakes, and firms make mistakes, and that is just part of the deal. But colleagues who regularly provide poor recommendations reduce their influence at the decision table (and should not be interviewing job candidates).

Experienced managers and executives, regardless the industry, focus on this "bottom line" by whittling down what they look for in candidates to a few key traits, the first impression, and a few phone calls. Firms want job candidates to be sources of information, insights, and solutions; they do not want job hunters looking to simply plug empty holes in the organizational chart.

Interviewers have concerns, which you must address when answering questions. Answer questions in the most positive way and position yourself for the offer. Demonstrate, during the interview, that you can help the organization, that you will inspire trust with colleagues, and that you have a real interest in the role.

Phone Interviews

While the interview preparation and etiquette discussed previously applies to phone interviews, there is a key difference from traditional interviews: both parties cannot see each other. Preparing and participating in phone interviews centers on taking advantage of this difference. While you cannot see their reactions to your answers, they cannot see what materials lie before you, what notes you are taking (and what you are wearing). Therefore, the keys are to prepare your environment (the place where you will take the call), your materials, and your answers for telephone interviews.

Preparing for Telephone Interviews

For prescheduled phone interviews, consider the following steps to prepare yourself and your environment for optimizing your interview performance:

Minimize potential distractions. Turn off call waiting on your telephone; turn off the ringers on other phones (i.e. cell phones); turn off radios and televisions; inform roommates or neighbors, as appropriate, that you have an important call; place a "Do Not Disturb" note on your door.

Make yourself comfortable for the call. Prior to the expected call, go to the bathroom and wash your hands and face. Have water available during the call. Clear your throat. Once the call begins, there will not be opportunities to visit the restroom or get a drink.

Organize your materials. These include your resume (with notes emphasizing the skills and experiences you want to highlight), a list of key points about yourself (including reminders about specific examples and relevant stories), summary materials about the job and the employer (prepare these materials yourself; just printing pages off a website will not be useful because the relevant information will not be edited down or internalized), and a list of questions you would like to ask during the interview.

Rehearse answers to questions that you will likely be asked. Be prepared for a conversation regarding your background and skills.

In a phone interview, the ability to listen closely to the interviewer's comments and questions, the quality of your answers to these questions, and the confidence in your voice create powerful impressions. The materials you prepare offer available support for answering questions with strength and with meaningful examples. Other materials to have nearby include several working pens, a notepad, a calculator, and your calendar.

During the Interview

Phone interviews tend to be shorter than live interviews. (There is less chit-chat.) A phone interview is simply a focused conversation. To make the most of it, consider the following strategies that will make you sound more professional and energetic:

Do not smoke, eat, drink (except for a little water here and there), dip, or chew gum. All of these can be heard over the phone and distract from your answers.

Smile. Feelings and energy follow action, and the act of smiling comes through in your voice. It projects positive energy and interest through the phone. Some folks also recommend standing up, saying your voice sounds stronger. (Personally, I like to take notes and work with my materials, so standing becomes difficult. Others swear by it.)

Speak slowly and directly into the phone. Enunciate clearly. This is especially applicable if you are conducting the call over a speaker phone or cell phone. Use the technology the way it was designed to be used.

Listen carefully. Do not interrupt the interviewer. If they want to do all of the talking, let them.

Respond to questions when you are ready. It is perfectly acceptable to repeat or paraphrase the questions to make sure you understand what is being asked. It also demonstrates your listening skills. Take the moments you need to collect your thoughts before answering. Interviewers do not award bonus points for responding quickly; they are not on the other end holding a stopwatch.

Avoid "uh"s or "um"s. This habit is especially noticeable on the telephone. Take a breath or pause if you need a moment to gather your thoughts.

After the Interview
Say "thank you." Write a brief thank you note which restates your interest in the job. The goal of a phone interview is to arrange a face-to-face interview. After thanking the interviewer, ask if or when it would be possible to meet in person.

Informational and Research Interviews

Informational interviews serve to gather information and develop relationships. Informational interviews provide job seekers and researchers one method for tapping into the experience and knowledge of others. We schedule these interviews with individuals who have specialized information and for an insider point of view on an industry or firm. For recent graduates, informational interviews provide an opportunity to get your head around what opportunities exist in the workplace and what people actually do in a work setting. Direct communication with those on the inside gives us insight and a feel for the real issues in a business.

While interviewing skills can be learned, the keys are to prepare and to practice for the interview. How?

Write an interview guide. This is the single most valuable way to prepare. Whether 30 minutes in person or 15 minutes on the phone, know what you are going to ask. It is your responsibility to make the most of the time available. When developing your guide, consider this approach:

1. Brainstorm questions you think you need answers to.
2. Group the questions by topic/category.
3. Step back, and ask "What do I really need or hope to learn in this interview? Why do I want to talk to this person?" Defining the purpose of the interview helps you order and phrase the questions correctly.
4. Given the purpose, refine the questions and categories.

Start with general questions and move to specifics. Begin with general questions about the industry, for example, before getting specific about the person's tenure and responsibilities.

Study/research the firm and interviewee. Learn about the interviewee prior to the interview. Know his background and education and reputation. Find out where he is from. He is doing you a favor by setting aside time to meet with you; it is your job to be prepared.

Adhere to informational interview etiquette:
• Do not, under any circumstances, exceed your requested time, but be prepared to stay longer if the person is willing.

- Dress as if it were an actual job interview. First impressions are always important.
- Get to your appointment a few minutes early and be courteous to everyone.

Take the initiative in conducting the interview. You ask the questions, you interview the person. Ask open-ended questions which promote a discussion and cannot be answered with one word. Listen and guide. Let the person know that you are listening. This can be done through body language, by nodding, or leaning forward. Avoid body language that indicates a lack of interest, such as folding or crossing arms, slouching, or looking around the room. *Turn off that cell phone and don't check it.* Take notes, and keep the pen moving.

Request referrals. (e.g., "Can you suggest other people I might talk to?") This is especially important if you are conducting research or seeking job opportunities.

Say "thank you." Write a brief note which restates your appreciation for this person's time. Note something of particular interest from the interview and state how the interview helped you move forward in your research or career development.

Resume Preparation and Cover Letters

When sitting down to prepare a resume, put yourself in the shoes of the person who will receive it. Think of yourself as the user of the resume, not the producer. Remember. the purpose of the resume is to get an interview. The resume and cover letter should clearly summarize your background and experience in an easily digested format to help the user make a decision about whether or not to talk to you.

The resume is often the first point of contact between you and a potential hirer. The clarity of the structure, the directness of the writing, and the relevance of your background will be digested by a human resource manager in approximately 7 seconds. While 7 or 8 seconds appears insufficient to judge your entire background, it is sufficient for the reader to determine whether or not your resume is acceptable (easy to read, well organized, correct spelling) and whether or not you have the proper background and experiences to be considered for this job.

Stop reading and count out 7 seconds. One one-thousand, two one-thousand, three one-thousand....seven one-thousand. Is that enough time to look over a resume for the first time and assess whether or not the resume looks good, and whether or not the candidate has sufficient or suitable experiences to be considered for the job? Yes, it is. Understanding this helps us rebuild our resume for a competitive evaluation. The resume should cleanly and clearly share our best, most relevant experiences. It is the quality, and not the quantity, of our activities, jobs, and accomplishments that attract the interest of hiring managers.

Our resumes serve us best when their structure draws no attention. The less time the reader spends thinking about how the resume looks, the better. We want most of the 7 seconds to be spent assessing our credentials, and less time reflecting on fonts. We want the manager to be sufficiently interested to spend 8 or 10 or 30 seconds thinking about our qualifications, and setting our resume aside in the "good" pile or forwarding it on to colleagues. Do not use fancy colors or funny pictures. Leave resume art to artists. A natural resource resume, as most resumes, cleanly summarizes who we are and what we have done that makes us qualified for the job. It is not the whole story; it is a clean summary of relevant highlights.

Executives and operating managers may have particular qualities they look for in a resume that have less to do with the content and more to do with personal preferences or the structure. One job recruiter explained to me the importance of "white space" and font size. He said the resume "should have good spacing and borders, so it does not look cluttered" and "a font big enough so it's not blurred by a fax machine." He said the resume from a promising job candidate can get faxed around a firm quickly, and a resume packed with information in a small font will simply reduce the usefulness of the document. As to font size, he told me "10 is the absolute minimum." An executive in a forest products firm told me he dislikes small fonts because "I hate to put on my glasses."

A resume should be accurate. NEVER lie or exaggerate. Again, the document often represents the first point of contact between you and the hiring organization. If something is off about the resume – a document that you created based on your experience in your own words – how can the firm trust you with a role in their firm? Facts can be checked. Hiring managers do call colleagues or alumni of your program to find out what they know about you. We operate in a small universe, and an erroneous resume sets a bad precedent for entering the work force.

The resume acts as a functional document for the interview process, and a single misrepresentation sinks your canoe. I conducted an interview once where the candidate had noted "fluent in Spanish" at the bottom of the resume. I asked, in Spanish, where he had learned to speak, and it quickly became clear that the person was not fluent. He said he was "rusty." I asked him what else on the resume was not accurate. Interview over.

Know your own resume. One manager seeking to fill an entry level forest resources slot in 2002 told me about a recent interview where, after a brief scan, he knew the resume of the candidate better than the candidate did:

Interviewer: "I see you had a summer job working for an auto supply shop."

Candidate: "I did?"

This lack of familiarity with one's own resume sends several signals, all bad. How accurate is this resume? Who prepared it? When? Why isn't this person prepared? The resume introduces your background to the employer; it should help you communicate what you want to communicate during the course of the interview. Preparing for the interview includes reviewing your own resume so that you can talk knowledgeably and succinctly about each experience. Use each item on your resume to highlight skills and provide brief, specific examples regarding your accomplishments. The resume is the chip for your dip.

Items in the top third of the resume get the most attention. Items on the left margin will be seen first, next those on the right margin, and then those in the center. What does that tell us? If we are coming directly out of school, our education is most important (so it goes at the top), along with the career objective (what we want), then followed by our strongest work experiences.

Most resumes are organized in one of two ways: chronologically or functionally. A chronological resume, listing your most recent experiences first, is more common and relevant for those following a discernable career path in a given and/or related industry. These resumes are intuitive and easily followed. "Ah, I see your last job was here and then you got promoted, and before you did that for a while...."

A functional resume, one that organizes your experience by skill or accomplishment, works well in two specific situations. One case is where your work history has gaps that would be highlighted in a chronological resume. "I see here that you dropped off the face of the earth from 1999 through 2002." Breaks in work history can occur for all sorts of reasons, such as illness, travel, children, jail.....and they may or may not be relevant or important to the interviewer. However, a functional resume keeps the discussion focused on what you DID accomplish and demonstrates how you can add value to this firm.

The other case is when applying for a role or project that requires a specific or technical skill. For example, you apply for a project leader role with the USDA and you understand that, in this case, the job requires a specific set of technical, communication, and project management skills. As a result, you choose to organize your experience on the resume by these categories. This also becomes relevant if you are applying for roles or positions within the same firm, or applying for a temporary or contract role. In these cases, the interviewer wants someone who has the specific skills needed to get the job done today, not someone who requires training or handholding. In these situations, a functional resume can prove useful.

Writing the Resume

Keep the resume simple and straightforward. [See Appendix 4 for an example] At the top, list your name and contact information. List an email address that you check and a phone number that has voicemail. Use a professional-sounding voicemail message.

State a clear career or job objective. While not required, it is helpful. The resume should make your case for a specific job. A brief statement near the top of the resume clarifies for the interviewer what you want to do. If you cannot state, in one or two sentences, what you want to do, how can you expect the interviewer to figure it out for you? The career objective should be specific, with reference to both a job function and the industry.

There are differences of opinion regarding the use of career objectives. While a clear, specific statement of your career objective will rarely hurt (unless the hiring manager thinks your statement does not match the job), it helps most in cases where:

1. You are making a career switch or applying for a job that does not match your major,
2. Your background or major is broad and general (such as management or communications),
3. You are applying for a project or a functional role within a firm, and
4. You are applying for an internship.

An effective objective statement is specific. It states what type of role in which industry you are seeking, and states what you bring to the job. Do not use vague objectives like "To work in the field in which I completed my studies." Do not state that you "seek an entry-level" position. Barbara Marchilonis, director of the career counseling program DBM Real World 101, says "Why belabor the obvious?" Here are examples that are specific without being overly restrictive:

- Work with landowners to meet their forest management objectives.
- Obtain a forest resource position where 3 years of finance experience will add value.

- Conduct applied research in wildlife biology and natural resources.

If you are graduating from college, avoid including high school activities, unless they represent directly relevant experiences or remarkable achievements. For example, you may have started a business, been a nationally ranked athlete, or excelled as a mechanic or musician. Hiring firms don't care about your high school grade point average or club memberships. If you are 22 or 23 years old, the hiring manager wants to know more about how you've spent the past four years than the past eight. If you are a mid-career professional, the firm wants to know what you accomplished in your previous jobs.

List degrees in reverse chronological order. There is no need to list non-degree institutions, places where you studied that do not offer degrees, or where you did not receive a degree, unless you want to establish a geographical tie or training in a particular area.

When listing experiences on your resume, consider the following guidelines to strengthen the impact and clarity to the reader:

Use present tense for current jobs and past tense for previous jobs. Current job: "Manage three forestry technicians." Previous job: "Scaled and sorted logs for export and domestic markets." Mixing verb tenses on the resume can confuse the reader and shows a lack of attention to detail.

Be specific and action oriented. Each phrase should lead with an action verb and describe a specific responsibility. Action verbs show the reader you actually did (or do) something and create a picture of productivity and activity. "I" is understood and unnecessary. For example, remove "I" from the phrase "I conducted research on fertilizer and herbicide applications."

Highlight accomplishments. Recent graduates tend to undersell their accomplishments. Include awards, achievements, or the completion of significant projects. Brainstorm a range of relevant accomplishments with a friend or relative to help identify those skills that may not seem significant to you but might be interesting to an employer. Examples might be if you worked on a farm and learned to run heavy equipment, rebuilt engines, or volunteered as a Big Brother or Big Sister. Activities that indicate leadership, initiative, and persistence, and the ability to work independently or with teams add to your qualifications. These include activities that broaden your network or demonstrate interest in your field, such as the Wildlife Society or the Society of American Foresters.

Quantify whenever possible. Using numbers gives a sense of scale and emphasizes the specificity of what you achieved. Numbers add tangibility. While GPAs, if used, should never be rounded, you can round sales numbers or budget sizes. "Managed the sales team" does not tell the tale as well as "Managed 6 sales representatives who generated $20 million annually."

Certain items should not be included in a resume. While you do not need to write "references available upon request" (it's assumed), you may add an additional sheet of paper with references if you want. Avoid including your age, or family or marital status (in the United States, it is illegal for firms to ask about these items). Avoid any mention of salary requirements, and do not include pictures.

Two-page resumes are okay, but *one-page resumes are best.* A one-page resume forces you to focus on the best and most relevant experiences you have to offer. The resume should not be exhaustive. Firms do not need or want to know about everything you have ever done. Always continue to tailor your resume and have several versions for different outlets..

There are two exceptions to the one-page rule, and they both relate to the academic and research market. If you apply for any sort of academic or research role – such as a professor, scientist, researcher, or graduate student – additional pages may be acceptable and expected for listing publications, grants, and awards. The second exception relates to applying for grants and scholarships. The key question here is, "Who will be judging and reviewing my resume?" If the committee is made up of academics and PhDs, send in the longer version. They are used to, and may expect, more details about your every activity and publication.

Joann S. Lublin spoke with career coaches about student resumes and summarized her findings in an April 29, 2003 *Wall Street Journal* article, "College students make job-hunting tougher with weak resumes." Common mistakes by students include:

1. *Writing generic job descriptions that omit tangible accomplishments.* Folks want to know what you did and what you initiated. Highlight promotions, quantifiable accomplishments, and unique aspects of the role. They invite questions and separate you from other candidates.

2. *Selling short other assets.* For students, consider combining extracurricular activities with work history and listing it all under "experience", if you have strong items like fraternity or sorority president, club founder, treasurer in charge of collecting dues or handling budgets, or volunteer someplace where you developed tangible skills.

3. *Listing experiences in chronological order.* This can put stronger items towards the end of the resume. Then employers may overlook significant experiences because they scan resumes for just 7-8 seconds. List them in *reverse* chronological order.

4. *Filling resumes with extraneous information.* Students frequently fill two pages, twice the optimum length, with unnecessary information such as "references available upon request." Also, do not waste space with height, weight, low grade-point averages or widely held computer skills. If you cannot use Microsoft Word, stop reading this and go learn.

In October 2002, Lynn Woodward, a retired industry executive, spoke at a Forest Business Seminar at the University of Georgia about the attributes required for a successful interview. He opened with "Good credentials and a one-page resume." Your experience and background summarized neatly can provide a powerful starting point for getting an interviewer interested in you. The purpose of the resume is to obtain a job interview. The resume must spark enough interest for the employer to learn more about you. Otherwise, it fills the recycling bin.

Writing Cover Letters

Always include a cover letter when submitting your resume. It is proper business etiquette and it provides an opportunity to separate you from fellow applicants. It allows you to introduce yourself in a way that cannot be conveyed in the resume. Also, it tells the hiring firm exactly why you sent them your resume (which is not always obvious).

Hiring managers may not read the cover letter at first, but others will. The cover letter shares more about your style, professionalism, and ability to write – a CRUCIAL skill – for the manager interested in calling you in for an interview. You can summarize unique skills and qualifications, and the process of writing the letter helps clarify what you are doing and why, and how to explain it. Writing is a great clarifier for others, and for yourself. In short, the cover letter can definitely help you and, assuming it's well-written and error free, will not hurt you.

The cover letter is not a simple repeating of your skills and experiences. Rather, it explains how your unique qualifications match the needs of the firm. Avoid a string of sentences that start with "I" or "My", but put yourself in the shoes of the firm and CONCISELY address what you can do for the employer. If you don't know what the employer needs, conduct research or talk to others in the field. Also, the importance of demonstrated writing skills cannot be overemphasized. The cover letter is the ultimate writing sample for a job applicant.

Use a three paragraph format. [See Appendix 5 for an example]:

- Paragraph one answers the question "Why am I writing?" It identifies the position you are applying for and how you heard about it. Lead with your strongest connection to the employer.
- Paragraph two answers the question "Who am I and why should you hire me?" It identifies specific matches between your background and the needs of the employer. Provide additional details about one or two of your qualifications to highlight what you can do for them.
- Paragraph three answers the question "What is next?" It refers the hiring manager to the attached resume and clearly states your next step, such as an intention to follow up and your specific and strong interest in the job. Tell them you are available to visit and interview in person. A cover letter should never, ever be more than one page.

Customize the cover letter to the job for which you are applying. At a minimum, include the correct company name, job title, date, and contact person. When a job posting does not provide a specific contact name, call the firm and find out the manager's name. Avoid using "To Whom it May Concern" or "Dear Sir" or "Dear Sir or Madam." If no contact name is available (and sometimes the job ad states "no phone calls"), settle for "Dear Hiring Manager." Note the desired job skills and qualifications, and match them to your background.

In describing your background, be specific. The firm is not concerned with your birthplace or favorite food, but would be interested in specific accomplishments that indicate how you could help them. Citing one or two specific responsibilities, accomplishments, or relevant projects can provide a powerful incentive to take a closer look at your resume.

The letter must be error free. No matter your qualifications, spelling or grammatical mistakes turn the letter into a liability. Spell the firm's and the hiring manager's name correctly. Sign the letter. Use quality paper, preferably the same type on which you printed the resume. Get someone else to review your letter, and check for grammatical, spelling, or logic mistakes.

Remember, be prepared and sharpen the most important skill prior to venturing into any interview situation – listening. Interviewers will judge your engagement in the conversation and your ability to answer the questions they asked, and to acknowledge non-verbal cues such as body language or glances indicating it's time to wrap up an answer or a conversation. Success in these areas depends on employing active and accurate listening skills. We were given one mouth and two ears; use them proportionately.

References

The following references have been helpful to me and were used as references for this chapter:

Bolles, Richard N., *What Color is Your Parachute?* Ten Speed Press. Berkeley, CA. 2005, 400 pages.

Feibelman, Peter J., *A Ph.D. is Not Enough!* Perseus Publishing, 1993, 116 pages.

Johnson, Tory, Robyn F. Spizman and Lindsey Pollak, *Women for Hire: The Ultimate Guide to Getting a Job.* Penguin Putnam, 2002, 324 pages.

Medley, H. Anthony. *Sweaty Palms: The Neglected Art of Being Interviewed.* Ten Speed Press, 1993, 468 pages.

Strunk, William, Jr. and E.B. White, *The Elements of Style*, Longman, 2000.

Appendix 1: Questions You Might Ask
During an Interview

In what areas is the company trying to improve?

To whom would I report?

Could you give some examples of projects I would be working on?

How much travel is involved?

Will relocation be required?

What kind of assignments could I expect in the first 6 months?

What products (or services or stores) are in the development stage?

Is this a new position or will I be replacing someone?

What qualities are you looking for in a candidate?

What characteristics do successful employees in your company share?

Please describe the advancement opportunities.

What growth areas do you foresee?

Could you describe your training program?

How frequently are performance appraisals done?

What would a typical day be like?

How much contact is there with management?

Appendix 2: Common Interview Questions

Think about your answers to these questions and practice them prior to your interview. Develop answers and practice them aloud. Even experienced speakers recognize the value of rehearsing sentences and ideas in preparing for expected questions.

What are the responsibilities of your current or previous position?
What do you know about this industry? What do you know about our company?
What is your most significant accomplishment?
Why are you leaving your present position? Why did you leave your last job?
Why do you want to work for us?
Tell me about yourself.
Why should we hire you for this job?
What was the last book you read?
What leadership/supervisory roles have you held?
What is your weakness? What is your strength?
Of what accomplishments are you most proud?
Why did you choose this particular field of work?
What have you done that shows initiative?
What do you see yourself doing in 5 or 10 years?
Tell me about other jobs you've had. In hindsight, how could you have improved?
What are your long-range career objectives and how do you plan to achieve them?
What makes a good supervisor?
Describe a few situations in which your work was criticized.
Are you analytical? Give an example.
Are you a good manager? Give an example.
Are you a leader? Give an example.
Have you hired people before? What do you look for?

Appendix 3: Questions Interviewers Should Not Ask

Potential employers are not permitted to ask a range of questions during interviews because of Employment Law Issues associated with potential discrimination for age, race, religion, marital status, and gender. These questions include:

How old are you?

What is your birth date?

How do you feel about reporting to someone younger than you?

How long have you resided at your present address?

When did you graduate from high school?

What are the ages of your children, if any?

What is your marital status?

What was your maiden name?

Do you prefer to be addressed as Miss, Ms, or Mrs?

What is your spouse's name? Occupation?

What are your child care arrangements?

How do you feel about significant business travel? (This can be asked, but only if it is asked of all candidates.)

What was your father's surname?

Have you ever served in the armed forces of another country?

Do you own or rent your place of residence?

Do you own a car?

Do you have any outstanding loans?

Have you ever declared bankruptcy or had your wages garnished?

Of what groups or organizations are you a member?

Are you able to work weekends? (Discriminates against those whose religions prohibit them from working Saturday or Sunday)

Have you ever been arrested?

Did you receive other than an honorable discharge from the military?

Appendix 4: Partial Sample Resume

Phillip N. Groovey
611 Belle Court
Athens, GA 30606
706.987.8707; **pgroovey@forestry.uga.edu**

OBJECTIVE   Develop a career in forest management and timberland investing.

EDUCATION   **University of Georgia** Athens, GA
                 Master of Forest Resources, Forest Finance, May 2004

                 University of California at Berkeley, Berkeley, CA
                 Bachelor of Science, Forestry and Natural Resources, May 2000

EXPERIENCE
2004 – Present   **FORISK CONSULTING, LLC**, Athens, GA
                 Consultant & Market Coordinator
                 • Manage AL and MS markets for quarterly Wood Demand Report
                 • Coordinate data collection and analysis for 160 forest industry facilities
                 • Support research on forest operations and timberland investments

2000 – 2002   **NACOGDOCHES FOREST RESOURCES,** Jefferson, TX
                 Resource Forester
                 • Planned all land management and procurement activities for 30,000 acre unit
                 • Coordinated weekly area forecasts and wood flows (~30,000 tons)

Summer 1999   **NATIONAL PARK SERVICE**, Point Reyes, CA
                 Seasonal Worker, Point Reyes National Seashore
                 • Cleared and maintained trails and signage

HONORS and SERVICE
     2003   Xi Sigma Pi Forestry Honor Society, University of Georgia
     2000-Present   Society of American Foresters – Treasurer, Bulldog Chapter

ADDITIONAL SKILLS
     Computer: Access Database, ArcView, SIMS

Appendix 5: Sample Cover Letter

October 22, 2000

Charles L. Brown
Director of Acquisitions
Forest Finance Partners
17 Red Light Center, Suite 1313
Jackson, MS 39232

Dear Mr. Brown:

As we discussed over the telephone on Monday, I am interested in the Forest Analyst position at Forest Finance Partners. I believe that upon review of my enclosed resume you will find that I am well qualified for this position.

My qualifications include a master's degree in addition to professional experience. As a graduate student, I studied finance, accounting and real estate as well as their application to forest management and timberland investment. As a timberland appraiser, I performed numerous market research studies and financial analyses to assist clients with investment decisions. As a resource forester with Nacogdoches Forest Resources, I gained significant experience in all aspects of wood procurement and forest management. I enrolled in graduate school specifically to study and obtain a position in the field of timberland investment; this is such an opportunity.

My enclosed resume more completely presents my qualifications. Thank you for your time and favorable consideration. I look forward to hearing from you.

Sincerely,

Phil N. Groovey

Chapter 3:
Negotiating

We make our fortunes and call them fate.

Benjamin Disraeli

Negotiation depends on communication. Think of a negotiation as starting an ongoing two-way relationship. In a salary negotiation, we look to improve our situation – to satisfy needs – while building trust. How we represent ourselves while negotiating with our future manager or supervisor provides an indication of how we will represent the firm in the future. The successful negotiation, then, requires proper preparation, a sense of etiquette, and correct timing.

Why negotiate? You get and deserve what you ask for. If you do not ask for the aisle seat instead of the middle on the airplane, if you do not ask for leather seats instead of cloth in the car you are buying, if you do not ask for a higher starting salary that better reflects your experience and the current market, they will not be handed to you.

Professional negotiator and writer Herb Cohen puts forth a three-question "negotiating litmus test" regarding when you should negotiate:

1. Am I comfortable negotiating in this particular situation?
2. Will negotiating meet my needs?
3. Is the expenditure of time and energy on my part worth the benefits I can receive as a result of this encounter?

For those of us negotiating salary and benefits for full-time employment, the answers to the questions above should be yes, yes, and yes. If we are uncomfortable, we need to get comfortable through preparation.

This chapter focuses on negotiating a starting salary and benefits package. It assumes that we have received an offer, and it provides procedures for preparing and getting comfortable with the salary ne-

gotiating process. You do not have to be an expert negotiator to improve your starting salary; rather, you require an understanding of basic negotiating tactics and preparation. I repeat: you do not need to be
an expert to succeed; you need to be informed.

Getting Prepared

Prepare yourself for salary discussions and negotiations through
research. The greatest tool in any negotiation is information. My Dad
always emphasized to me the importance of "facts, not speculation" in
a negotiation. Once you receive a job offer, new information must be
gathered. At a minimum, collect the following:

Salary averages in your industry, job type, and geography. Sources
for this information include alumni, professors, friends of the family,
and peers. If you are a student, you have access to excellent resources
that, later in your career, you will wish you still had easy access to.
Career centers, libraries, staff, and professors exist, in great part, to
help you, if you ask for it.

Professors receive calls year-in-and-out from managers looking
for job candidates and, at times, to discuss salary and benefit
expectations. Also, students who receive job offers often share that
information with professors to get feedback and perspective on how
this offer stacks up and what else should be considered. Alumni
can also provide knowledgeable feedback, particularly if you have a
personal connection through school events (such as tailgate parties,
award banquets, and society meetings), projects, or internships.

*Salary ranges of the offers received by peers and classmates this year
and last.* Again, college students are in an excellent position to quickly
gather substantial amounts of useful information. Talk to your friends,
and to their friends, about existing job offers. While it may be "none
of your business," you do not need, though you would prefer, specific
numbers and details of offers they received. What you do need to
know is, for example, if the job pays in the $28,000 - $32,000 range or

the $38,000 - $42,000 range. Collecting this type of information from several sources will enable you to get your arms around the market. [See Appendix 1: Salary Research on the Internet]

Employer's compensation guidelines. Try to obtain information on the employer's standard benefits package so that you have information beyond salary. Alumni, industry colleagues, and classmates can help here. For large companies and government agencies, benefits information is often available directly from their websites. If firms or agencies have human resource managers, call them and ask for a general benefits overview. This is a standard question, and one they answer daily.

Identify norms in your field as to which items are negotiable and which are not. Check the Occupational Outlook Handbook, company web sites, and the Career Center at your university. Take advantage of your alumni network, make phone calls, and ask basic questions to learn more about current standard practices.

Decide on the minimum salary (be realistic) that will satisfy you. Unless you are an NFL first round draft pick or an established investment banker, it is impractical to walk into a starting salary discussion without a clear understanding of what you <u>need</u>. How much money must you earn to satisfy the basic needs of your family? Author Richard Bolles notes that understanding your situation is as important as understanding the market.

To prepare, establish a rough budget, including rent, food, utilities, insurance, car and recreation, and account for taxes. If the potential jobs fail to meet or exceed this amount, keep looking.

Receiving and Evaluating the Offer

When the job offer is made, avoid negotiating. This is an exciting moment! Your hard work preparing the resume and cover letter, and your performance in the interview, resulted in the job offer you sought. First, thank the employer for the offer and express your strong interest in the job. Then, request time to evaluate the entire compensation package. Ask, "How much time can I have to consider the offer?" Most employers will give you time. If they don't, consider this a red flag. The following is a process to use for receiving and evaluating the offer:

Delay salary and benefit negotiations in the interview process. Your power to negotiate increases as the field of candidates reduces to just you. When should you negotiate? After the offer and before you accept it: that's when you have the most leverage. It is only through making you an offer that the firm explicitly says, "We want you."

If you have no intention of accepting the offer, move on. Do not waste your time or the company's resources by entering into negotiations. Students: what you do also reflects on your school, classmates, and alumni. Operate in good faith, but keep good notes.

Consider the pros and the cons of the offer. Make sure you want this job. It may help to create a chart that includes, at a minimum, the following:

- **Salary**: regular, overtime.
- **Non-salary compensation**: signing bonus, profit sharing, stock options.
  - **Note**: be careful with respect to annual bonuses. These are not guaranteed. Ask what the typical bonus has been the last couple of years, and what happens if you have a good year when the company has a bad year.
- **Benefits**: paid vacation (number of days, when they can be used, when you can start using them), personal days, sick days, insurance (medical, dental, vision, life, disability), company truck or automobile allowance, professional training and continuing education (tuition reimbursement), professional memberships.
- **Relocation expenses**: house-hunting, temporary living allowance, closing costs, travel expenses, spouse job-hunting/re-employment expenses.

- **Job specifics**: responsibilities, title, location, supervisor, travel, starting date.

This outline helps clarify your understanding of the offer and pinpoints areas of concern. It results in a type of "pro-con" list of what you like and dislike about the opportunity.

Developing a Counteroffer

Again, recognize that you have your greatest negotiation leverage between the time the employer makes the original offer and the time you accept the final offer. Once you accept, you have little to no room to negotiate, so consider the offer carefully against your job requirements.

Prepare a prioritized list of items you want to discuss regarding the salary and benefits package. This is your cheat sheet for the negotiations and should include the specifics of the what, why and how much you are looking for. Use the pro/con chart you made to evaluate the offer for developing the list. This list could include:

- **Base salary**. For entry level roles, negotiate salary first, and then move on to other elements of the offer. Dick Daniels, a Professor of Forestry at the University of Georgia and former Research Scientist for Westvaco, says "The best retirement plan is a high salary." Ask for a higher salary than your target so that when the employer counters your proposal, the salary should, at a minimum, approximate your original goal.
- **Signing bonus and salary review**. Ask for a salary review after three months rather than six months or a year to qualify for an early raise.
- **Benefits**. For some firms, cash compensation is not negotiable, but benefits are more flexible. Vacation time, when you can start using vacation, and educational opportunities are often negotiable.
- **Relocation expenses**. This can come in the form of cash or reimbursed expenses. If the firm handles these expenses directly, ask if they are "grossed up."

- The IRS may treat relocation support as additional income and can tax you accordingly. By grossing up these expenses, the firm effectively handles the potential tax liability.
- **Job specifics**. Starting date, job title, and equipment (vehicle, type of computer, cell phone) are potential items that may be important to you.

While preparing your counter proposal, include a few benefits that are expendable so that you can drop them in a concession to the employer as negotiations continue. What you want to know going into the negotiation is the employer's true limit. Through research or discussions, any insight into the maximum salary or benefits available reduces your guesswork.

Negotiating a Final Agreement

The purpose of a salary negotiation is to determine the most that an employer is willing to pay to hire you. How do we go about this? With lots of information – facts, not speculation – and a positive attitude. Remaining clear and focused on this purpose enables us to eliminate unproductive and useless actions. For example, do not judge the actions and motives on the other side of the table. Avoid all opportunities to humiliate, embarrass, or offend the counterparty. Stay cool and, please, keep the discussion in perspective. Specifically:

Enter negotiations with a positive attitude. Remember, you may be negotiating with your future supervisor. Stay polite. Try to make it a win-win situation. You want a better deal, but you also need the employer to feel as though they got a good deal as well.

Know your "wedge." The firm or agency offered the job to you, not to someone else. Understand why. You may have exceptional language skills, technical skills, communication skills, or field experience. This "wedge" separated and separates you from your peers, and has value.

Consider the following approaches to open the negotiation process:
- Approach 1: I am very interested in the position, but I would like to discuss the salary you are offering.
- Approach 2: I really want this position, but I was a little disappointed that the offer was lower than I expected.
- Approach 3: I am very excited about this role, but was hoping the starting salary would better reflect my (a) (graduate) education or (b) work experience.

Support your case by stating your skills, the average salary range for your level of experience in your field, and the average salaries for college graduates or professionals in your field. Then, let the employer respond and continue the discussion from his lead.

Never make demands; ask questions. Raising questions and making requests keeps the negotiation conversational, not confrontational. The strategic issues to consider while preparing for the negotiation include deciding what questions to ask, how to ask them, and when to ask them. Politely ask questions for clarification and to understand options.

Ask questions about standard benefits packages. Just because it was presented to you in writing on fancy paper in a laminated folder does not mean items such as vacation, relocation, or tuition reimbursement are not negotiable. If it's important to you, ask.

Emphasize the personal. As one person told me, "It's easy for people to shaft others if they don't see them in personal terms." Do not allow yourself to become a statistic. Remember your wedge. Build a relationship.

A former communications student of mine named Max told the following story in class about negotiating:

> A few years back I went to a yard sale in my home-town. At this yard sale I found a very nice, but used,

Quantum Energy reel on a very nice Pflueger rod. Since I am a serious bass fisherman, I knew I had to have this rod and reel. The price was $75 for what might cost $200 new. But I decided to see if the owner would come down any. I began to talk with him about fishing and how much I enjoyed it. He told me that he enjoyed it as well, but just didn't have time to fish anymore. After talking a while, I told him I was interested in this particular rod and reel and offered him $55. He stood there for a minute thinking about it and let me have the pair for $65.

Max made it personal by turning a negotiation into a conversation between two guys who both love fishing.

Be prepared for any possible reaction to your counter proposal, from complete acceptance to agreeing to some concessions to refusal to negotiate. Herb Cohen says, "Don't allow yourself to be manipulated or intimidated by those who aren't concerned with your best interests." The person might say yes to everything, or might get angry. Remain positive, remain polite. How you are treated during the interview says something about how you will be treated in the future.

Accepting the Offer

A conversational negotiation about a starting compensation package will tend to be a short negotiation. Entry level positions with natural resource agencies and forest industry firms have limited negotiable items. They tend to have standard starting packages, so once you get beyond the negotiable items, wrap up the talks. This means understanding when to stop. Successful negotiations do not produce fireworks and a chorus lines. They are practical, nuts-and-bolts conversations where everybody wins something.

Once the employer agrees to your compensation requests, the negotiations are over. You cannot ask for more in good faith. Be excited, shake hands, and accept the offer.

Get the final offer in writing. This is non-negotiable and a standard and expected business practice. It protects both sides and ensures that everyone involved has a common understanding of the terms. DO NOT officially accept the job without getting the final offer in writing. Be wary of companies that are not willing to do so.

Telephone Negotiations and Pay Raises

The phone rings. You answer it and hear, "Hi! This is Phil Groovey from Nacogdoches Forest Resources and I was calling to finalize the terms of our offer to you." The firm that offered you a job wants to negotiate and you feel compelled to comply. Do not do this. In telephone negotiations, callers have the advantage. They are prepared; you are not. Politely say that this is not a good time, that you have another appointment, that you are occupied. Ask, "When would be a good time for me to call you back?"

Telephone negotiations, like telephone interviews, tend to be shorter and may produce additional misunderstandings. Risk comes with speed. Without the benefit of body language and eye contact, both parties have difficulty perceiving inclinations or commitment. And short, quicker negotiations can produce terms without the benefit of time to consider them.

Be the caller. This lets you plan and prepare. If the other party insists on calling you, or needs to call you for logistical reasons, agree to a specific time.

Listen. Do not play solitaire while participating in a telephone negotiation. Listen carefully and take notes. Ask about points you are not clear on. Date your notes and save them.

Get it in writing. We always get offers in writing. This is paramount for phone interviews. The written document will provide the only proof and recourse that you and the firm understand exactly what was agreed to.

Once you are in a job, keep track of your accomplishments, publications, presentations, initiatives. Use a small notebook or your Palm Pilot/PDA to note them on a weekly basis. Why? This will help you prepare for job reviews and pay raises. The issue here is that your manager is unlikely to carefully record your accomplishments, and when it comes time for your annual review or time to discuss raises or promotions, you can summarize the achievements in a one-page memo or fact sheet. The bottom line: unless you track your noteworthy accomplishments, it's unlikely anyone will.

References

Bolles, Richard N., *What Color is Your Parachute?* Ten Speed Press. Berkeley, CA. 2005. 400 pages.

Cohen, Herb, *You Can Negotiate Anything.* Lyle Stewart Inc., Secaucus, NJ. 1980. 255 pages.

Nierenberg, Gerard I., *The Art of Negotiating.* Hawthorn Books, NY. 1968. 195 pages.

Overstreet, H.A., *Influencing Human Behavior.* The People's Institute Publishing Company. 1925, 296 pages.

Appendix 1: Salary Research on the Internet

Going to Google and typing in "salaries" generates a flock of salary research websites. Before you do that, try these free sites that have been posting salary information for years:

www.bls.gov/oco
The Bureau of Labor Statistics surveys individual salaries across a range of occupations through the "Occupational Outlook Handbook." This site summarizes these results and provides them in a searchable database. This site also provides links to detailed information on salaries across industries.

www.salary.com
This may be the biggest salary site out there. It features a "Salary Wizard" that allows you to search by job title and geography. The site also provides additional resources for employers looking to get a better handle on the market. Dozens of other sites use this Salary Wizard, including Monster.com.

www.salaryexpert.com
This site also features a salary calculator, and it sells reports and surveys that include information on international salaries, alternative salaries, and salaries in the non-profit sector.

Chapter 4:

Phones, Cell Phones, Voicemail, and Email

A few years ago, while sitting in Atlanta's Hartsfield airport waiting to board a flight to Washington, D.C., I saw Georgia Congressman John Lewis sitting nearby. A man approached him, introduced himself, and started telling Congressman Lewis about his business activities and concerns about government. While talking, the man reached to his belt, plucked a Blackberry from its holder, and began scrolling through, checking, and RESPONDING TO email messages. Congressman Lewis patiently listened to and calmly watched the man multi-task.

In this case, a member of Congress was slighted. But it should not matter whether it is an executive, a teacher, or your spouse. Who is more important, the person standing in front of you or the unknown person calling from 2,000 miles away?

In 2000, I worked on a forest products consulting team led by Julio Hernandez. Whenever we met to review our work, he gave me his undivided attention. He did not answer the phone when it rang. He set aside his cell phone. He did not check email or look at his laptop computer screen. He looked at me or at the work itself, and really listened to what was being said. This tended to make our sessions short and efficient.

We forget how these forms of electronic communication have unintended consequences (i.e. ringing in meetings, interrupting conversations, reducing personal time, and generating clutter). They can be disrespectful and annoying, as well as inefficient and impersonal. This chapter reviews the basic, and minimum, rules of etiquette for the types of electronic communications that have become inseparable from our work environment.

Phone Calls and Speakerphones

In forestry – whether research, business, or public management – the first contact with colleagues, clients, and citizens is often over the phone. Poor impressions of you will occur from being disorganized, impolite, and unfocused. Alternately, you can appear sharp and competent by being polite and professional. In the end, you want to present yourself in the most professional way possible. To be effective on the phone remember these points:

Have a purpose. When making an outgoing call, know what you want to discuss. Have the necessary documentation at hand. This may include order forms, credit cards, or details about your specific request. This saves time. Remember, effective phone calls are short phone calls.

Limit social conversation. Social chat may include noting the weather or the upcoming football game, but, taken to extremes, it wastes time. It can be frustrating if you have a lot of work to do. Busy people often prefer a clean cut, direct approach with a bare minimum of social chat.

Give concise answers to questions. Long rambling answers are unprofessional, dull, and confusing. *If you don't know an answer, say so.* If someone relies on you when you are guessing, and you guess wrong, then they will never trust you again. If you do not know something, say you will get back to them with a firm answer and reference.

At the end of a call, summarize key points and next steps. This ensures that both people agree on what has been said, and know what action will be taken next.

Don't talk to anyone else when on the phone. You would not do this when talking to someone in person, why would you do this to someone on the phone?

Don't answer the phone while eating. This sounds muffled and unprofessional.

Don't talk, surf the internet, or read while talking on the phone. We can tell when someone else is multi-tasking, and they can tell when we do it to them. Shorten the call by taking care of business; then get back to your crossword puzzle.

Always call back. It is frustrating to wait for a promised phone call. By not returning a call, you show disrespect and impede the other person's work, especially if they depend on your answer.

A note on speakerphone etiquette:
Always ask permission to use the speakerphone, and be sure to identify other people in the room. In the past, I have been both "let in" on a call where the speakers on the other end did not know I was listening and "listened in on" when I did not know others were listening to the call, and I don't like either one. It is dishonest and unprofessional. Some procurement foresters never discuss prices or negotiate contracts on wireless phones or speakerphones for concerns such as these.

Voicemail

Leaving a voicemail message is an art developed over time. Make the message short, clear, and to the point. Say your phone number early and repeat it at the end. Spell your name if the person doesn't know you. Provide a good time to call back or an email address if appropriate.

Used wisely, voicemail benefits us. It can be used to receive a message after-hours, thereby reducing the need for further conversation. However, do not hide behind voicemail. If callers constantly reach your voicemail instead of you, they will suspect that you are avoiding calls. Here are a few tips on such things as greetings and responding to voicemail at work.

Record your own voicemail greeting. Do not use the default or have Ed McMahon record your greeting; callers will doubt that you check your voicemail.

Include your name and department or firm name in the greeting. That way people know they have reached the correct person.

Record an alternate message when traveling. Also, forward your line directly to voicemail. Then callers don't have to wait through unnecessary ringing before leaving a message for you.

Check messages daily and return messages within 24 hours. If it will take longer than 24 hours, call the person and advise. Callers should consider you responsive and know that you check your voicemail regularly.

When leaving voicemail messages for others:

Speak clearly and slowly. The listener needs time to process information and write it down. It is frustrating trying to figure out a muffled or quickly stated phone number. Then you have to keep replaying the message.

Immediately identify yourself. "This is Phil Groovey from Forestry Associates."

Leave your call back number next. Even if you know the person has your number, they may not have it handy or be calling from another location. Use full phone numbers with area code.

Keep messages short and to the point. 'The reason I am calling is...' Get to the point and hang up. Don't ramble. Do not describe a problem or situation and cause the person to have to keep replaying the message. Voicemails should be no longer than 30 seconds. Period.

Cover one topic in one message. Specify what you want the recipient to do.

Avoid phone tag. Specify what you want the recipient to do or to know. This wastes time. Don't ask the person to call you back if you can provide the information they need in the message. If you want them to call you back, let them know when you will be available.

Anticipate voicemail and plan your message. When calling someone, assume you may have to leave a message. Think about the key point and write down a few key words prior to making the call.

Provide your phone number again. You stated it at the beginning; now give it again slowly. This provides another chance for the person to jot down the number without replaying the message.

Hang-up before putting down the handset. To hang up, use your finger to press the release button. Using the handset can create noise. Also, you may fail to actually hang up the phone, and the voicemail on the other end keeps recording.....

Be careful what you say. Your recorded voice message can be forwarded to others. Think about what you say and what tone you use. Electronic voicemails are so slick now that the message you leave can be forwarded all over the world.

Cell Phones and Blackberries

Cell phones are for YOUR convenience, not everyone else's. When lecturing, teaching, or meeting, I turn off my cell phone. My colleagues, clients, and family know this. I check messages in the interims. Turning off cells should be as automatic as getting that drink of water and using the restroom prior to a meeting, interview, or class.

Cell phone etiquette is easy and straightforward. Follow these two rules:

Lights off, phone off. Do not use cell phones in theaters or at the movies, during weddings, class, meetings, or presentations. Do not check cell phones if you are the person in front of the room. This happens!

People first, cell phone second. If you are talking to someone in person, do not answer your cell phone. Do not check to see who is calling. Who is more important? What message does that send? Sometimes you are expecting an important call; let the person you are talking to know that this is the case.

   Other tips:
Maintain a distance from anyone while talking. Consider it "personal space."

Avoid talking in elevators, libraries, museums, restaurants, dentist or doctor waiting rooms, or places of worship. Avoid celling in auditoriums or other enclosed public spaces, such as hospital emergency rooms or buses. Please avoid emotional conversations in public...

Don't use loud, long, and annoying ring tones. You are not a one-man band and I didn't pay to hear a concert.

Avoid "multi-tasking" by making calls while shopping, banking, and waiting in line or conducting other personal business. Please be safe – avoid driving and celling; we all know it's dangerous.

Tell callers when you're on a cell phone so they can anticipate distractions or disconnections.

Inform people you talk to regularly – especially clients, colleagues and family – how you handle cell phone calls. Ironically, managing your cell in a systematic way makes you more productive and responsive.

Never answer cell phones during business meetings. This includes interviews and meetings with co-workers or subordinates.

In sum, keep cellular calls brief and to the point.

A note on the Blackberry:

The Blackberry is the pocket-sized email device that allows users to check email in real time while traveling. Users find them so addictive that the handhelds are sometimes called a "CrackBerry." At a recent technology conference organized by *The Economist* magazine, "Crackberry" dependence was a hotter topic than web services.[3]

The BlackBerry invades meetings, interviews, and one-on-one conversations. People feel comfortable checking email under the table on the handhelds during meetings, while talking to someone standing right in front of them, and, for some reason, while presenting at conferences and meetings. To navigate a suitable path for benefiting from the BlackBerry while adhering to a modicum of respect for your fellow human being, apply the two Rules of Cell phone Etiquette to your BlackBerry use:

Lights off, BlackBerry off. Do not use the BlackBerry in theaters or at the movies (it is distracting to those sitting near you), during meetings or presentations.

People first, BlackBerry second. If you are talking to someone in person, do not check to see who sent that last message that caused the BlackBerry to vibrate. Who is more important?

Email[4]

Checking email eats time and costs money. For example, getting 40 emails each day and spending just three minutes each requires two hours. Before email, senders shouldered the burden of mail. Now readers shoulder the burden. Writing, stamping, and mailing a letter was a lot of work. Email undermined that system as every little thought and whim can become instant communication. The result: your Inbox has twelve-hundred messages.

Email is easily abused because it is easy to use. Checking and answering email is something you know you can do, so it provides an immediate sense of accomplishment. However, it crowds out those actions that could really move you ahead. Remember, the objective of email is to get it read and acted upon. Some tips for coping:

Check email at defined times daily. Check email randomly at your peril. Decide in advance exactly when you'll check email. I typically check mine twice in the morning, twice in the afternoon, and at night. Have a legitimate business reason for checking email as often as you do. For many people two or three times per day is sufficient.

Handle email in batches. Turn off email "autocheck." Let folks know that to reach you instantly, email may not be best. When checking email, shut the door, and crank through messages.

Use email for non-urgent communication. Email was not meant for emergency communicating. This is particularly true in natural resources. We may be in the field for long periods of time or driving long distances between regional offices. In desk-bound roles, email can serve this rapid-fire function. However, if time is of the essence, pick up the phone. If others pressure you to check email more often, let them know that they should not use email for urgent communication with you; pick up the phone or visit in person.

Use subject lines. People scan their inbox by subject. Make your subject rich enough that your readers can decide if it's relevant. I do not open emails immediately without subject lines unless they are from my wife, a current colleague, or a current client. Sorry Mom. [For emails from folks I do not know, if the email address or subject line does not speak to me, I delete it.]

For folks you work with regularly, *deliver the message in the subject line if possible.* Put your initials, END or EOM (end of message) at the end of the subject line to let readers know that nothing is in the text box. Example: "Subject: Meet tomorrow in my office at 10am – BCM"

This approach also delivers the message up front. For example, consider the subject line below. If you cannot make the meeting on October 4th, you delete and move on. If you can, you read the message to confirm the location and agenda.

Bad Subject	Good Subject
Forestry Club meeting	Forestry Club meeting 10/4 at 7 pm

Also, make sure readers understand your abbreviations. For example, 10/4 means October 4th in the United States. In Europe, 10/4 means the 10th of April.

Change the subject line when replying to messages. Sometimes you reply to a message just because it is addressed to the person you want to write to anyway. However, they will not know the nature of the message unless you change the subject. Know what I mean?

Make action requests clear. If you want things to get done, say so. This is especially true for emails copied to many people. We all hate getting copied on an email and finding out weeks later that someone expected us to do something. Be sure that everyone copied needs to receive the message. Then summarize action items so everyone can read them at one glance.

Bad CC	Good CC
To: Amanda, Liz, Tim Subject: Visiting ABC sawmill on 10/4	To: Amanda, Liz, Tim Subject: Visiting ABC sawmill on 10/4
We will visit ABC sawmill on 10/4. Let's check in with Joe Forester to see what time works best for him. For the visit, we will bring copies of the timber market research. Who wants to drive?	We will visit ABC sawmill on 10/4. - Amanda: Can you ask Joe Forester at ABC what time works best for him? - Liz: Please bring 6 copies of the timber market research. - Tim: Can you drive?

Edit forwarded messages. If someone sends you a message, do not forward it without editing. Make the message relevant for the ultimate recipient (and don't get the original sender in trouble).

Make emails one page or less and easily read. Ensure most of the email can be read without scrolling. Many people never read past the first screen. Use short paragraphs, bullet points and/or headings to separate ideas. FYI: the screen shows approximately one-half of a written page.

Create "reference" and "to do" folders and use them. Respond immediately to time sensitive messages; drag others to "to do."

Answer briefly. Reply to long messages with two words. "Thank you." "Go ahead." "Sounds good." "I approve." "Great idea." People will learn not to expect lengthy answers from you.

Understand context and use proper etiquette. While emails to friends and family can be informal, emails to executives, clients, and professors should reflect the context of your relationship as to deciding whether or not to use titles or first names. For example, students might avoid starting emails to their professors with, "Hey, you" (this happens).

Do not attach lengthy files when the reader needs but a few key points. As the sender, you make the decision about whether the attachment is relevant to the receiver. Save them time and effort, and note the specific passage or table that they should look to. Provide context for attachments or forwarded messages. Put yourself in their shoes; what would you prefer?

Do not use emoticons (symbols expressing emotions) or chat room jargon in business email messages. Your readers are interested in getting the facts. [Plus, it hurts my neck to keep turning sideways to figure out what those symbols mean:)]

Proofread, proofread, proofread before hitting send. Email is a form of business communication. Use the spell checker. Even mynor airers make you look bhad.

Use good sentence structure, punctuation, and grammar. They make it easier for the reader to read quickly and they leave a good impression of you.

DO NOT USE ALL CAPS. Adopt a business-like tone and use simple, straightforward language. (ALL CAPS LOOKS LIKE FLAMING!) If you emphasize everything, you emphasize nothing.

don't type in all lower case (unless you are e.e. cummings). it is not proper english. ask your english teacher.

Do not forward inappropriate jokes, stories, or pictures. Once forwarded, you assume responsibility for the content. You may be surprised to find where your messages may end up. Remember that employers own their email systems and can legally inspect anyone's email.

Don't FLAME or spam in email. It's unprofessional to lose control in person; to complain and go off in writing makes the situation worse. Soon, readers will stop opening your messages.

Did I mention to proofread?

DOS and DON'TS Summary

Do	Don't
• Use subject lines • Edit forwarded emails • Make action requests clear and emails short • Proofread	• Send chain mail to business colleagues • Attach unnecessary large files • Spam, FLAME, or BCC your readers • Forward inappropriate jokes or stories

References

Lindsell-Roberts, *Sheryl. Strategic Business Letters and E-mail.*
    Houghton Mifflin Company. Boston, MA, 2004. 374 pages.
Robbins, Stever. 2004. Tips for mastering email overload. Available
    at   http://hbsworkingknowledge.hbs.edu/item.jhtml?id=4438
    &t=srobbins

Chapter 5:
Meetings

One either meets or one works.

Peter F. Drucker

Meetings that do not produce tangible results for you, me, and every other person in the room suck energy and commitment from projects, jobs, and companies. The scheduling of meetings, and making people attend meetings, often say more about who needs to demonstrate authority, who wants to obtain authority, and who does not have enough to do (or know what to do). In short, meetings often fail to serve the explicit, needed functions that they are designed to satisfy.

Purpose of Meetings and Why they Fail

Meetings have necessary, valuable and SPECIFIC roles to fill. These include:

Rapid decision making. David Sharman, author of *The Perfect Meeting*, highlights the role of effective meetings to bring together personnel to discuss and resolve issues that could significantly affect staff. If a decision must be made quickly, it provides a final check that all relevant, known facts are on the table.

Share information. Sharing information in person, rather than through memos or emails, benefits from the opportunity to engage in two-way communication. For example, changing security procedures at an office benefits from explaining in person why this is important and how it helps the group. It provides opportunities to brainstorm methods for implementing changes.

Sharing information includes updates on changes with clients and the external business environment. The PROBLEM with information sharing at meetings comes when valuable information is not shared, when the meeting is poorly run (unorganized and too long), and when other agendas are met through the meeting. These meetings should be tightly run with an agenda distributed in advance so attendees know what to expect.

Generate ideas. Meetings can be useful working sessions. Jack Welch, former Chairman and CEO of General Electric, organized meetings to "wallow" in data on a specific market or business opportunity and to identify courses of action for moving forward. The work teams were cross-functional with a range of experiences.

As a researcher, I worked with a team studying opportunities to centralize log trucking operations in middle Georgia. We had weekly meetings to brainstorm insights and address issues. As our paper worked its way through the peer review process, reviewers across the board complemented our insights in the analysis, and these were the direct products of our planned work sessions. The key to successful meetings of this sort include a planned agenda, clearly communicated expectations about what one needs to do to come prepared, clear understanding of who needs to attend and why, and a clear understanding of the time frame and expectations. Good meetings foster quality work relationships, as they enable a common understanding of relevant information and a sense of purpose for decisions and strategies.

Why do meetings fail? Meetings fail for three primary reasons.
- One, meetings fail because the purpose of the meeting was unclear. If the purpose of the meeting cannot be clearly identified, the meeting was either unnecessary or poorly thought through by the organizer. If the purpose of the meeting is unclear, it is difficult to ensure that the right people are in the room, and that the wrong people are not in the room. Never, ever go into a meeting without knowing what you want the outcome to be.
- Two, meetings fail because they are poorly planned. This includes ill-conceived and unconsidered logistics. For example,

the environment was not conducive to meeting because there were no chairs or flip charts, or the meeting was disrupted by the construction activities outside. Worse, no agenda was prepared or distributed.

- Three, meetings fail because they are poorly run. They start late and end late. The facilitator may have been inadequate. Agenda integrity was not maintained. At the end of the meeting, nothing was decided and no one was better off. That's the litmus test.

Organizing and Leading Meetings: Setting Agendas

Meetings should not be held just because they have already been scheduled and are on the calendar. (Though there may be team building benefits to holding meetings for groups that don't see each other regularly.) A clearly defined purpose and objective justifies every meeting. In reality, meetings represent the conclusion, not the beginning, of the work. Meetings provide the opportunities to check in, update the team, make decisions, and delegate new tasks.

They say the three most important things in real estate are location, location, location. The three most important things for a successful meeting are outcome, outcome, outcome. The question to answer prior to scheduling and planning a meeting is, "What should be the outcome of this meeting?"

Answering this question identifies the key concerns and need-to-knows with meeting planning and execution. It results in identifying the purpose, being clear about who needs and does not need to be at the meeting, and determines the timing and location of the meeting. This ensures that those who need to be there can make it and that the meeting is scheduled in advance of when things must be decided while also providing enough time to let folks finish what needs to be done before the meeting itself.

In college, I ran for President of my fraternity largely on the platform of holding shorter chapter meetings. Previously, our meetings lasted three to four hours and included the serving of food and beer. Meetings were poorly attended and the general understanding of issues facing the House was low. We instituted changes for preparing and conducting meetings that included:

- Officers submitted written summaries of their oral reports prior to the meeting,
- Officers each had one minute to report two things:
    1. What they did since the last meeting, and
    2. What they will be doing between now
       and the next meeting.
- Food and drinks were distributed after the official business, and
- Meetings started on time.

The meetings were not perfect. They lost their "social" feel, and freshman felt as if they had walked into a boardroom setting. However, the changes let us get the work done in advance and spend the meetings updating the guys, making decisions, delegating tasks, and voting. That semester, the typical meeting lasted less than an hour. By starting on time and conducting business efficiently, guys could budget an hour in their schedules before getting back to lab. For guys with time on their hands, they could attend the meeting before watching Monday Night Football.

To improve the efficiency and effectiveness of team meetings, incorporate the following guidelines in your planning and facilitation:

Specify meeting objectives. People should know why the meeting is being held and what the expected decision outcomes will be. No objective means no meeting.

Provide and distribute agendas in advance of meetings. This helps (potential) attendees decide if they need or want to be there, and reminds folks to be prepared, especially those with specific tasks and items assigned in the previous meeting.

Remind participants about meeting requirements or responsibilities. If reports are being given or handouts distributed, as a courtesy remind those responsible.

Begin meetings on time. If nothing else, prepare an agenda and start the meeting on time. This sets the stage and establishes a precedent for proceeding. The message, which I explicitly state when teaching classes, is "you help me start on time, I will get you out of here on schedule."

Maintain "agenda integrity." John Tropman, author of *Effective Meetings,* lists three steps to maintaining agenda integrity. One, there is an agenda. Two, all agenda items are discussed. Three, items not on the agenda are not discussed. End of story. The agenda provides a means for managing a reasonable schedule of items during the meeting and may include budgeted times for discussing items.

Discourage food during meetings. But serve or permit beverages. Food is distracting, messy, and noisy. Provide food before a meeting, after the meeting, or during scheduled breaks. Coffee and other drinks, however, seem to provide a necessary lubricant for team meetings.

Ask, "Who else needs to know?" As the meeting comes to a close, ask the group who else needs to be made aware of the information shared or decisions made during the meeting. Then assign someone the role for making sure this happens.

End meetings on time. Everyone will thank you. The expectation of ending on time will help you facilitate discussion and decisions during the meeting. Participants in well-run meetings appreciate the abbreviated chatter and reduced repetition common in free-for-all meetings.

Establish the proper precedents for productive meetings with the first meeting you schedule in your role as a leader, manager, and facilitator. [See Appendix 1: Preliminary Checklist for the Perfect Meeting] Prior to that first meeting, contact participants about the meeting, and confirm that their concerns or topics are included on the agenda, if necessary. The meeting must be relevant to everyone in the room. Otherwise, those individuals do not need to be there, or the meeting is unnecessary. Prepare and distribute the agenda in advance and confirm the starting time and place of the meeting. Finally, start and end that first meeting on time.

As the meeting facilitator, your responsibilities include distributing the agenda, reminding those attending the meeting of their responsibilities, and taking care of the logistics of the meeting (i.e. schedule and prepare the room). During the meeting, you maintain agenda integrity, keep the discussion moving by facilitating and clarifying discussion, and bring discussions to a close to make decisions. In the end, participants will thank you for keeping the discussion from going around in circles.

The meeting represents the end and not the beginning of the process. The real work gets done before the meeting. The meeting is for updating and educating the team or for making an informed decision. The planning and preparation required to support successful meetings frees the team, rather than constrains it.[5]

The process also provides a means for managing and mitigating disturbances. In practice, troublesome participants create problems in a meeting because they can. And they can because there are no rules, no clear expectations, and no facilitation. In a way, the squeaky wheel is doing you a favor and telling you, in front of the team, to get your meeting process in order. If the team agrees on the meeting rules and norms, then the person who flouts those rules is not only disrespecting you as the facilitator, but is holding up progress for the entire team.

Common Elements of EFFECTIVE and INEFFECTIVE Meetings

Effective	Ineffective
• Detailed agenda with assigned roles	• Goal unclear or not specified
• Starts and ends on time	• No agenda
• Clear meeting norms and rules	• No time limits on discussion
• Periodic process checks by facilitator	• Facilitator participates, not facilitates
• Decisions made	• Participants arrive unprepared
• Next steps identified and roles assigned	• No decisions or assignments made

Attending Meetings

Never go to more than two meetings a day
or you will never get anything done.
Observation #150 from *Never Confuse a Memo with Reality*

Ask questions at company meetings, but don't embarrass anyone.
Observation #309 from *Never Confuse a Memo with Reality*

As participants in meetings, we have responsibilities to come prepared and support the norms agreed to by the group in maintaining meeting effectiveness. Generally, attending and participating in meetings effectively includes the following:

Arrive on time. You know what time the meeting starts and the other attendees and the facilitator are probably colleagues of yours. Arriving on time is the least you can do.

Turn off your cell phone or set it to vibrate. Ringing and answering cell phones are disrespectful to the group (unless it's understood and expected as part of your role).

Be prepared. Bring a pen, notepad, and your calendar. If there is any chance in the world the meeting will include a few numbers, bring a calculator. Also, be prepared to discuss the agenda items by reviewing them in advance.

Participate. Listen with an open mind and take notes. Avoid interrupting others and contribute relevant points to the discussion. That is why you were invited and why you agreed to attend the meeting in the first place. If you plan or need to leave the meeting early, inform the leader or facilitator.

Avoid side conversations or digressions. Like ringing cell phones, they are disruptive and disrespectful to the group.

In sum, avoid the black hole of endless meetings by leading and participating in meetings in ways that facilitate work, not interrupt it. Identify the expected outcome of each meeting. Use this to plan the agenda and determine who needs, and does not need, to attend. Distribute agendas in advance to inform participants of what may be required of them so they can prepare and participate as expected. Establishing and implementing procedures for effective meetings will improve information flow and decision making within any organization.

References

Moran, Richard A. *Never Confuse a Memo with Reality*. Harper Business. New York, NY. 1993. 164 pages

Sharman, David. *The Perfect Meeting*. Wings Books. 1993.

Tropman, John. *Effective Meetings: Improving Group Decision Making*. Sage Publications, Inc. 1995.

Appendix 1: Preliminary Checklist for the Perfect Meeting

This checklist is based on "The Perfect Meeting – Preliminary Checklist" on page 7 of David Sharman's <u>The Perfect Meeting</u>. The purpose of this checklist is to ensure that all participants know and understand the purpose of the meeting and its desired outcome.

- Develop and distribute an agenda.
  - o This provides the framework upon which the meeting rests and is organized to achieve its purpose and outcomes.
- Identify the participants.
  - o Those with insights or expertise are invited to attend, along with those who have the authority to implement agreed upon actions.
  - o Participants come prepared, understand their roles, and are able to make contributions in an open and positive way.
- Use a facilitator (chairperson).
  - o The facilitator guides the discussion with reference to the agenda, accommodates the needs and sensitivities of those present, and keeps the meeting heading in the direction of the desired outcome.
- Agree upon actions.
  - o Before the meeting ends, the facilitator should summarize the decisions made, the next steps agreed upon, and the responsibilities of the participants in the meeting.
- Follow-up.
  - o The meeting secretary records all the decisions and action points in the minutes, so that everyone can see what they are required to do.

Chapter 6:
Giving Feedback

*Feedback, n: a) a process in which the factors that produce a
result are themselves modified, corrected, strengthened, etc. by
that result; b) a response that sets such a process in motion*
                                Webster's dictionary

Why is Feedback Important?

Giving feedback provides a means for correcting and reinforcing behaviors. To focus on the right things at work, employees need and want to know what they are doing well. They also need to know when and what they are not doing well so they can change instead of worrying about job security or what the manager thinks. The desire for reinforcing feedback resides in all of us; the need for constructive feedback in any organization cannot be overstated.

We need feedback to improve. Managers who do not provide feedback to employees and colleagues produce two unwanted consequences. One, they fail to reinforce desired behaviors and performance. Two, they enable unwanted behaviors and consequences. If anyone – whether working for, with, or above you – receives the same feedback, or no feedback, for a range of behaviors, unwanted outcomes are often the result.

For example, offering indiscriminate praise destroys the power of positive feedback. Walking into the office every day and telling everyone, "You're doing a great job!" without being specific has no value over the long run. There is often a right way to do things and a wrong way, or there are expectations and standards as they relate to your team and clients. These expectations must be communicated and reinforced.

Failing to provide feedback keeps poorly performing employees performing poorly and undermines confidence in the firm's leadership among the best performing employees. People then realize there are no consequences associated with bad performance and unreliable rewards associated with good performance. Everyone sees this happen and the managers lose credibility and respect. The team assumes managers do not know what is going on or, if they do, they cannot or will not do anything about it. At the end of the day, people need to know what they do well, and where they need to improve. Without honest, accurate feedback, how can management expect anything?

If feedback is so important, why do managers avoid giving it? Giving feedback can be difficult. Managers want to avoid debates and confrontation. They don't want to hurt feelings and/or they fear failing to effectively offer feedback and ending up in a worse situation than where they started. Ineffective working relationships indicate poor communication and a lack of open, specific, and actionable feedback. Regular constructive feedback within an open, trusting relationship provides the most direct way for establishing and maintaining effective working relationships.

Preparing to Give Feedback

Before giving feedback on anything, managers and employees must have an idea of what success or failure looks like. My Dad reinforced for me the importance of having "shared expectations" up front so that all parties understand what is expected. Then you decide and define what success is, what it looks like when it is delivered, and how it will be measured. You give feedback based on these measures of success. Most feedback should be associated with items for which expectations have been clearly communicated. Shared expectations are important.

In natural resources, as in business generally, systems and processes provide different types of feedback. In a forestry operation, feedback can take the form of scores from safety audits or check cruises, or production bonuses. For wildlife or fisheries research, feedback may come through peer review or the acceptance and rejection of grant applications. However, at the end of the day in all professional settings, individual performance and behaviors are open to positive and constructive feedback from supervisors and colleagues.

Feedback must be timely. If you give me negative feedback on something I've been doing for three years without comment, then who is at fault? Once expectations have been established, give feedback regularly, whether good or bad. Feedback provides transparency. It forces managers to clarify where everyone fits into the scheme of things. It shows you know what is going on. It demonstrates that the person and the work are important. Feedback delayed is feedback denied.

Giving Constructive Criticism

Corrective, constructive criticism is harder to provide than positive, reinforcing feedback. Done poorly, it can be unnecessarily confrontational and emotional. Giving effective, constructive criticism involves three discrete steps:

1. Meet privately one-on-one and state the purpose of the meeting.
2. Be specific about what's wrong and how it must improve (relative to previously agreed upon expectations or the needs of the team).
3. Reinforce the trust and confidence you have in the person, and the role they play on your team.

Let's discuss each of these in more detail:

State the purpose of the meeting. "I want to give you some feedback on your work." Do not give feedback over lunch; give feedback during a private session, one-on-one. A feedback session is not a long conversation. It is brief, specific, and to the point. Feedback within a long or rambling discussion dilutes the purpose and power of the feedback. Deliver the message in a single, focused conversation. No small talk. Get to business.

Be specific about what's wrong and how it must improve (relative to expectations or the needs of the team). Simply saying what's wrong is not corrective, and does not explain why the behavior is problematic. Focus on behaviors, not the person. Constructive criticism should focus on specific actions or behaviors that the person can change or do something about.

Be specific about the behavior and give examples. Avoid generalizations like "You are always late." These are easily countered with one example. Don't say, "You are rude." Say, "When Mr. Jones arrived at our store, you did not greet him or shake his hand." If an employee failed to provide enough details or figures in a project proposal, specify what kind of additional information was needed. Then ask questions to confirm their understanding of the feedback. Focus on the behavior and actions you want changed, not the person.

Reinforce the relationship. The criticism concerned an action or level of performance, not the person. Do not rationalize the behavior for the person or analyze the situation. You want a change in behavior, not to conduct a therapy session. Your message is that you value the person, but not the specific behavior or performance in question. This is part of an ongoing, productive working relationship.

It is kind and honest to let employees know exactly where they stand. Effective feedback requires direct, truthful communication. Now this can be more direct than people are used to, but the most successful teams and organizations communicate directly. This type of directness at work requires an honest, open relationship built over time. The relationship exists in part because feedback takes place, and the feedback helps maintain the relationship.

Feedback Guidelines

Whether giving positive or constructive feedback, we benefit from being prepared and keeping in mind certain considerations. These include:

Gather the facts before giving feedback. Understand that there may be a misunderstanding. Ask why they are doing something a particular way. You may learn something.

Lead by example. Ask for and seek feedback. Thank folks for helpful criticism.

Avoid the "praise sandwich." This approach says to give positive feedback before and after any constructive criticism. This strikes me as disingenuous and insincere. How can I give strong, reinforcing positive feedback before corrective, constructive criticism? Which will you hear and remember? I don't know and don't care because I figure it won't be both.

As someone who has been on the receiving end of a "praise sandwich" or two, I view it as an unnecessary tease. Bells go off! Red flags cloud my vision. "Uh oh, he just praised me for something. Here comes the hammer...." Give specific, actionable feedback in a timely manner, and reinforce the relationship.

Understand the importance of context. Once when traveling by plane for work, I pulled out my laptop to finish something prior to landing. The person sitting next to me ordered a drink, settled into his chair, and tried to start a conversation.

"What are you working on?"

I politely responded, "Something for work."

Then he started reading over my shoulder and commenting, "Is that a proposal or something?"

I looked at him and said, "Is it all right if we don't talk?"

How did he take this feedback? He looked like he'd been shot. He mumbled an apology, sat back in his chair, ordered another drink, and did not say another word to me for the remainder of the flight. However, if I had to do it all over, I would have added, "My apologies, but I have something I need to finish before landing." I failed to account for context.

Avoid surprises. You should never surprise an employee or be surprised by a supervisor in a performance review or feedback session. Feedback is ongoing, not isolated to formal sessions every six to twelve months.

Give feedback in writing once or twice per year. While most communication at work is informal and most positive reinforcement and constructive criticism occurs on an ongoing basis, there are benefits to documenting once or twice per year in writing what your employees are doing well or what they can improve on. I do this to help me as much as the people that work with me. Not only does this provide an opportunity to recognize achievements and confirm that you know what is going on, it provides the employee an opportunity to confirm you are aware of their accomplishments. In cases where corrective action is required, it provides the necessary documentation to support ongoing improvements.

Summary DOS and DON'TS

Do	Don't
• Give feedback regularly	• Give feedback while angry or over lunch
• Gather the facts	
• Be specific	• Put off feedback indefinitely
• Reinforce the relationship	• Generalize
	• Serve a "praise sandwich"

Be Timely and Specific

If we abuse or lack the trust of colleagues and teammates, we will never have their permission to truly communicate with them. Therefore, give praise immediately, and be specific. Look for opportunities to praise and tell them exactly what they did well. Give constructive feedback immediately, and be specific. Tell them exactly what they did, how you feel about it, and how it can be improved. Review your shared expectations. Remind them of how important they are to you and to the team, that you value them. Then, it's over. Everything depends on being consistent and specific.

References

Blanchard, Kenneth and Spencer Johnson. *The One Minute Manager.*
Berkley Books. 1981. 111 pages.

Afterthoughts:

Leadership and Communication in Natural Resources

The people who are followed with commitment are those who are not afraid to experience and articulate reality.
Terry Pearce

In his book, *Leading Out Loud*, Terry Pearce argues that individuals are not followed because they have all the answers but because "They are perceived to have experienced the same confusion and contradictions as the rest of the population." Communicating openly and honestly, and acting in ways consistent with what is said, creates a sense of shared values and authenticity. This authenticity resonates with colleagues and community members, and lives naturally within so many natural resource professionals we work with.

In a way, each of us is a bundle of values and experiences wrapped in a personality. A key mission in life is to make our personality, and what our personality has to offer, effective in our particular environment of people and natural resources. Historically, it seems, this was less of a concern. As forest economist, David Newman, once said regarding the exalted reputation of forestry professionals when he was growing up, "Lassie's master worked for the Forest Service. You couldn't get much better than that!"

Natural resource leadership builds on an understanding of a common ethic, of respected values. Aldo Leopold, in his essay, "The Land Ethic," in *A Sand County Almanac*, refers to an evolution of ethical behavior in the following way:

> All ethics so far evolved rest upon a single premise:
> that the individual is a member of a community of

interdependent parts. His instincts prompt him to
compete for his place in that community, but his ethics
prompt him also to co-operate (perhaps in order that
there may be a place to compete for.)

Loving trees is not enough. We value professionals who work
hard, communicate openly with colleagues and members of the community, and seek collaborative solutions to forest resource management dilemmas. These natural resource professionals inspire others,
create cooperation, advocate ideas, and educate us. When we know
individuals who can be described this way, we call them leaders.

Endnotes

1. This can be particularly helpful in technical coursework. For example, when teaching computer-based short courses such as Excel for Foresters, getting to know the skill level and interests of the group helps my team know where we need to "hover" when providing one-on-one instruction during class. It also identifies skilled students who can offer support and real-life examples.

2. Excerpts from her letter to the editor, New York Times, May 3, 1994.

3. "The CrackBerry Backlash," *The Economist*, June 25, 2005. The article notes that the winner of the British version of the reality television show "The Apprentice" admitted that his wife threatened to flush his BlackBerry down the toilet.

4. Stever Robbins wrote an excellent article that covers more ground titled "Tips for Mastering Email Overload." The article is available at http://hbsworkingknowledge.hbs.edu/item.jhtml?id=4438&t=srobbins

5. Robert's Rules of Order is the bible of meeting rules and norms, providing a strict structure for managing meetings. David Sharman provides a summary of key points in Appendix 1 of his text.

CPSIA information can be obtained
at www.ICGtesting.com
Printed in the USA
BVHW07s1816180718
521943BV00008B/516/P